"THE BIG BET"

BEFORE CHARLES CHINIQUY WAS BORN, HIS DAD WAS STUDYING TO BECOME A ROMAN CATHOLIC PRIEST IN CANADA. BUT HE SAW SOMETHING HAPPEN IN THE CHURCH THAT UPSET HIM SO MUCH, THAT HE QUIT . . . HE STUDIED LAW AND BECAME A NOTARY.

AS HE WAS LEAVING THE PRIESTHOOD HE WAS GIVEN A GOING-AWAY PRESENT BY A CLOSE FRIEND.

GOD BLESS YOU, MY SON!

THANK YOU, FATHER

IT WAS A BEAUTIFUL FRENCH AND LATIN BIBLE.

HE REMAINED A DEVOUT ROMAN CATHOLIC; AND MARRIED REINE PERRAULT IN 1808.

A YEAR LATER LITTLE CHARLES CHINIQUY WAS BORN IN A SMALL VILLAGE, CALLED KAMORASKA, IN QUEBEC, CANADA.

5 YEARS LATER HIS FOLKS MOVED TO A PLACE CALLED MURRAY'S BAY . . . HIS MOM TAUGHT LITTLE CHARLES TO READ THAT BIBLE BECAUSE THERE WERE NO SCHOOLS.

DO YOU UNDERSTAND WHAT YOU JUST READ, SON?

YES, MAMA

BY THE TIME HE WAS 8 OR 9 YEARS OLD . . . HE HAD MEMORIZED . . .

- THE CREATION AND FALL OF MAN
- THE FLOOD
- SACRIFICE OF ISAAC
- HISTORY OF MOSES
- PLAGUES OF EGYPT
- THE HYMN OF MOSES AFTER CROSSING THE RED SEA
- HISTORY OF SAMPSON

- IMPORTANT EVENTS IN THE LIFE OF DAVID
- SEVERAL PSALMS
- ALL THE SPEECHES AND PARABLES OF CHRIST
- THE WHOLE HISTORY OF THE SUFFERINGS AND DEATH OF JESUS AS WRITTEN BY JOHN

WHEN IT RAINED SO HARD THAT FARMERS COULDN'T GO TO CHURCH . . .

THEY WOULD GO TO THE CHINIQUY HOME IN THE EVENING TO HEAR LITTLE CHARLES RECITE PORTIONS OF THE BIBLE.

THEY LOVED IT

AND MOSES SAID UNTO THE PEOPLE . . . FEAR YE NOT,

STAND STILL AND SEE THE SALVATION OF THE LORD!

BRAVO BRAVO

CLA CLA

THE FARMERS WERE TOUCHED. GOD'S HAND WAS ALREADY UPON THAT LITTLE BOY.

ONE DAY THE PARISH PRIEST CAME TO THE CHINIQUY HOME . . . THEY WERE THRILLED AND HONORED BY HIS FRIENDLY VISIT . . . BUT AN HOUR LATER . . . THE VISIT WAS NO LONGER FRIENDLY.

MR. CHINIQUY, IS IT TRUE THAT YOU AND YOUR CHILD READ THE BIBLE?

YES, SIR.

HE EXPLAINED HOW MUCH OF THE BIBLE HIS SON HAD MEMORIZED.

THE PRIEST WAS NOT IMPRESSED.

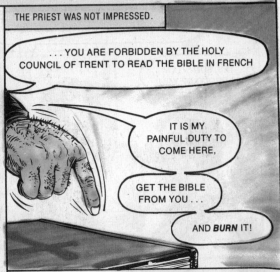

. . . YOU ARE FORBIDDEN BY THE HOLY COUNCIL OF TRENT TO READ THE BIBLE IN FRENCH

IT IS MY PAINFUL DUTY TO COME HERE,

GET THE BIBLE FROM YOU . . .

AND *BURN* IT!

WHEN THE PRIEST SAW MR. CHINIQUY'S FACE, HE GOT SCARED. LITTLE CHARLES NEVER SAW HIS DADDY SO MAD . . . THERE WAS DEAD SILENCE . . . HE GLARED AT THE PRIEST AND FINALLY SAID . . .

IS THAT ALL YOU HAVE TO SAY?

YES, SIR!

HE TOLD THE PRIEST WHERE THE DOOR WAS AND TO GET OUT *FAST*!

THE PRIEST TOOK OFF

MOOOO!

BUT THIS WAS *NOT* THE LAST VISIT THIS PRIEST WOULD MAKE TO THEIR HOUSE.

LITTLE CHARLES WAS SO PROUD OF HIS DADDY DEFENDING HIS BIBLE . . . HE KISSED HIM . . . JUMPED UP ON THE LARGE TABLE AND RECITED THE STORY OF DAVID AND GOLIATH.

"THEN SAID DAVID TO THE PHILISTINE . . . THOU COMETH TO ME WITH A SWORD AND A SPEAR AND WITH A SHIELD . . .

BUT I COME TO THEE IN *THE NAME OF THE LORD* . . .

IN HIS MIND, HIS DADDY WAS DAVID AND THE PRIEST OF ROME WAS THE GIANT THAT WAS STRUCK DOWN . . .

AT LEAST FOR THE TIME BEING!

3 YEARS LATER . . . YOUNG CHARLES HAD BEEN SENT TO A PRIVATE SCHOOL . . . HE WANTED DESPERATELY TO SEE HIS PARENTS . . . WHEN HE ARRIVED HOME HE WAS TWELVE YEARS OLD. HIS FATHER WAS DELIGHTED WITH THE PROGRESS HE HAD MADE IN SCHOOL.

IS MY GEOMETRY CORRECT, FATHER?

YES, SON . . . I'M *SO* PROUD OF YOU!

IT WAS A PRECIOUS REUNION . . . . THAT NIGHT THEY HAD FAMILY WORSHIP AND THEN ALL WENT TO THEIR BEDS FOR A GOOD NIGHT'S SLEEP.

AT 4 A.M. . . . HIS MOTHER SCREAMED!

OH NO!

. . . GOD . . . NO!

MAMA . . . WHAT'S THE MATTER?

OH, MY . . . DEAR SWEET CHILD . . . YOUR FATHER . . . IS DEAD!

UNGH

HIS POOR MOTHER FAINTED . . . A FRIEND TOOK CARE OF HER AS LITTLE CHARLES WENT TO HIS FATHER'S BED.

CHARLES PRESSED CLOSE TO HIS FATHER AND COVERED HIM WITH TEARS . . . HE COULD NOT BELIEVE HIS FATHER WAS GONE.

SOB

SOB

OH, FATHER . . . FATHER . . . COME BACK TO US!

HE PRAYED TO GOD FOR THE LIFE OF HIS FATHER. BUT HE WAS DEAD . . . HIS BODY WAS ALREADY COLD AS ICE.

TWO DAYS LATER HE WAS BURIED . . . HIS MOTHER WAS SO SICK WITH GRIEF, SHE COULDN'T EVEN WALK IN THE FUNERAL PROCESSION . . . IT WAS A TIME OF GREAT SORROW . . . HIS POOR MOTHER WAS NOW A WIDOW LIVING AMONG STRANGERS . . . HER STRONG, YOUNG HUSBAND WAS GONE, LEAVING HER WITH THREE LITTLE BOYS . . . SHE WAS WITHOUT A DIME AND HAD NO WAY OF MAKING A LIVING. HER HEART WAS BROKEN.

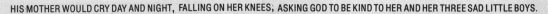

HIS MOTHER WOULD CRY DAY AND NIGHT, FALLING ON HER KNEES; ASKING GOD TO BE KIND TO HER AND HER THREE SAD LITTLE BOYS.

A FEW DAYS AFTER THE FUNERAL LITTLE CHARLES SAW THE PARISH PRIEST COMING TOWARDS THEIR HOUSE.

MOTHER . . . THE PRIEST IS COMING!

OH, THANK GOD

HIS MOTHER WELCOMED THE PRIEST AS AN ANGEL FROM HEAVEN.

EVERYONE KNEW THAT THE PRIEST HAD BECOME A RICH MAN.

SHE THOUGHT SHE WOULD GET HELP AND COMFORT FROM HIM.

DO YOU *STILL* READ YOUR BIBLE, LITTLE BOY?

YES, SIR.

THE PRIEST BLASTED HIS MOTHER ABOUT THIS UNTIL SHE BROKE INTO TEARS . . .

THERE WAS A LONG SILENCE . . . THEN THE PRIEST SAID . . .

MADAM, YOU OWE ME FOR THE PRAYERS WHICH HAVE BEEN SUNG,

AND THE OTHER SERVICES YOU ASKED FOR WHEN YOUR HUSBAND DIED.

I WILL BE *VERY* HAPPY . . . IF YOU PAID OFF THAT LITTLE BILL.

MR. COURTOIS, MY HUSBAND LEFT ME NOTHING BUT DEBTS;

PLEASE DO NOT TAKE FROM US THE LITTLE THAT IS LEFT.

MADAM, YOUR HUSBAND DIED SUDDENLY AND HE WASN'T PREPARED . . .

BECAUSE OF THAT HE IS IN PURGATORY.

AS THE CHURCH OFFERS PRAYERS AND MASSES . . . YOU *MUST* JOIN US . . .

BY GIVING ALL YOU CAN TO GET YOUR HUSBAND OUT OF PURGATORY.

I TOLD YOU . . . MY HUSBAND HAS LEFT ME PENNILESS . . .

IT'S *IMPOSSIBLE* TO GIVE YOU ANY MONEY.

HE PUSHED HER HARDER . . . SHE SAID SHE WAS SOON GOING TO LOSE THEIR HOUSE AND LAND.

ALL THE PRIEST WOULD SAY WAS . . . *YOU MUST PAY* FOR THOSE MASSES WE OFFERED FOR YOUR HUSBAND.

AFTER ANOTHER HORRIBLE, LONG SILENCE . . . SHE SAID . . .

SIR, DO YOU SEE THAT COW OUT THERE?

MOST OF THE FOOD MY CHILDREN GET . . .

YES.

COMES FROM THAT COW.

I HOPE YOU WILL NOT TAKE OUR COW (GASP)

IF THE MASSES YOU OFFER WILL HELP MY POOR HUSBAND'S SOUL IN PURGATORY . . .

AND WILL PUT OUT THOSE FLAMES . . .

THEN . . . TAKE OUR COW TO PAY FOR THOSE MASSES

VERY WELL, MADAM!

AND HE WENT OUT OF THE HOUSE.

MAMA . . . HE'S TAKING OUR COW! . . .

WE'LL DIE OF HUNGER . . .

WHAT ARE WE GOING TO DO?

MRS. CHINIQUY CRIED OUT IN GRIEF AS THE PRIEST AND THEIR COW DISAPPEARED.

SHE KNELT WITH CHARLES TRYING TO PRAY.

SOB SOB

I DIDN'T THINK THE PRIEST WOULD BE THAT CRUEL.

BUT HER SOBS CHOKED IN HER THROAT . . . SHE COULD NOT SPEAK . . . SHE TURNED PALE . . .

A COLD SWEAT CAME ON HER FACE AS SHE FELL TO THE FLOOR.

SHE WAS OVERWHELMED WITH GRIEF.

AFTER DRINKING SOME WATER, SHE REVIVED AND SAID TO LITTLE CHARLES . . .

MY SON . . . IF YOU EVER BECOME A PRIEST,

PROMISE ME . . .

YOU'LL ALWAYS BE KIND TO POOR WIDOWS.

I PROMISE, MOTHER.

CHARLES CHINIQUY DID BECOME A PRIEST OF ROME . . . AND HE NEVER FORGOT HIS MOTHER'S WORDS, NOR HER TEARS ON THAT TERRIBLE DAY.

SCRIPTURE: JESUS SAID: WOE UNTO YOU, SCRIBES AND PHARISEES, HYPOCRITES! FOR YE DEVOUR WIDOWS' HOUSES AND FOR A PRETENSE (A BIG ACT) MAKE LONG PRAYER: THEREFORE YE SHALL RECEIVE THE GREATER DAMNATION. MATT. 23:14

GOD HAD HEARD HIS MOM'S PRAYER . . . A FEW DAYS LATER SOME LETTERS ARRIVED.

OH, THANK GOD

THEY WERE FROM HIS MOM'S TWO SISTERS. ONE OFFERED TO TAKE IN HIS MOTHER AND 2 YOUNGER BROTHERS. THE OTHER, HAVING JUST LOST THEIR OWN LITTLE BOY, WANTED CHARLES.

CHARLES WENT BY BOAT TO HIS NEW HOME . . . WHEN THEY WERE SELLING THE FURNITURE, HIS BIBLE HAD DISAPPEARED . . . HE WAS SICK ABOUT IT.

SAYING GOODBYE TO HIS MOTHER WAS VERY HARD.

HIS UNCLE AND AUNT DIONNE WELCOMED HIM . . . THEY ASKED CHARLES WHAT HE WANTED TO BE WHEN HE GREW UP.

I WANT TO BECOME A PRIEST.

THEY ARRANGED FOR HIM TO STUDY LATIN UNDER THE VICAR* OF KAMORASKA . . . THE REV. MR. MORIN.

*AN IMPORTANT PRIEST IN TOWN

A FEW MONTHS LATER . . . HIS TEACHER ASKED HIM TO GIVE A SPEECH AT A BIRTHDAY PARTY GIVEN BY THE PARISH PRIEST*

HERE'S THE SPEECH CHARLES

*PASTOR OF A LOCAL CATHOLIC CHURCH

THE MOST IMPORTANT PEOPLE IN TOWN WERE INVITED. CHARLES WAS TO END HIS SPEECH BY GIVING A BOUQUET OF FLOWERS TO THE PASTOR.

CHARLES DELIVERED HIS MESSAGE AND THE PARISH PRIEST (MR. VARIN) WAS REALLY TOUCHED BY THIS ACT OF KINDNESS . . . LITTLE CHARLES REPRESENTED THE ANGEL OF THE PARISH . . .

SONGS WERE SUNG AND THERE WERE ABOUT FIFTEEN GENTLEMEN (INCLUDING PRIESTS) AND AS MANY LADIES . . . YOUNG CHARLES WAS ABOUT TO SEE A SIDE OF THE PRIESTS LIVES HE NEVER DREAMED EXISTED.

THE DINING ROOM WAS OPENED UP AND THERE WAS A LONG TABLE COVERED WITH THE MOST DELICIOUS MEATS AND WINES YOU COULD EVER FIND.

BECAUSE OF HIS LITTLE SPEECH CHARLES WAS ALLOWED TO JOIN THEM.

AFTER DINNER, THE LADIES LEFT THE TABLE AND WENT TO THE DRAWING ROOM, WHILE THE MEN BEGAN DRINKING TOASTS.

TO THE REV. MR. VARIN

TO MR. VARIN!

CHARLES DRANK ONE GLASS OF WINE AND HIS UNCLE SAID . . . "NO MORE! . . . OR I'LL MAKE YOU LEAVE THE TABLE."

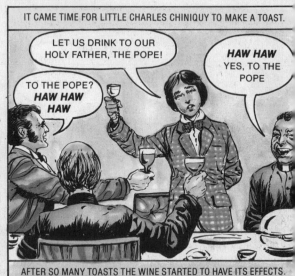

IT CAME TIME FOR LITTLE CHARLES CHINIQUY TO MAKE A TOAST.

LET US DRINK TO OUR HOLY FATHER, THE POPE!

TO THE POPE? HAW HAW HAW

HAW HAW YES, TO THE POPE

AFTER SO MANY TOASTS THE WINE STARTED TO HAVE ITS EFFECTS.

ONE PRIEST GOT UP FROM HIS CHAIR AND FELL HEADLONG ON THE FLOOR . . . . HIS TWO NEIGHBORS WERE TOO DRUNK TO HELP . . . EVERYONE WAS LAUGHING . . .

HAW HAW HAW

HAW HAW HAW

HIC

EXCEPT FOR LITTLE CHARLES. HE COULDN'T BELIEVE HIS EYES. THESE MEN OF GOD WERE DRUNK AND FALLING ON THE FLOOR.

WERE THEY REALLY MEN OF GOD?

WHO WOULD HAVE DREAMED THAT THE LITTLE BOY SITTING AT THAT TABLE THAT NIGHT WOULD SOMEDAY BECOME A PRIEST . . .

HAW HAW

HEE HEE

AND BE RESPONSIBLE FOR CANADA PASSING LAWS TO OUTLAW THE SALE OF LIQUOR.

CHINIQUY SAID ROMAN CATHOLIC PRIESTS TAKE GREAT CARE TO PREPARE CHILDREN FOR THEIR FIRST COMMUNION. CHILDREN GO TO CHURCH TO LEARN THE CATECHISM AND THE EXPLANATION OF ALL ITS TEACHING.* *FIFTY YEARS IN THE CHURCH OF ROME, PG. 37-38

MR. MORIN, WHO TAUGHT CHARLES LATIN, INSTRUCTED THE CHILDREN FOR THEIR FIRST COMMUNION.

LET US PRAY.

THIS IS THE FOUNDATION OF IDOL WORSHIP AND SUPERSTITIONS WHICH THE "CHURCH" OF ROME GIVES AS THE RELIGION OF CHRIST.

WITH THIS CATECHISM, ROME CORRUPTS AND SPOILS THE MOST SACRED TRUTHS OF THE GOSPEL.

ISN'T MARY BEAUTIFUL!

IT IS HERE THAT JESUS IS REMOVED FROM THE HEART OF THE CHILD AND MARY IS PUT IN HIS PLACE.

IT'S SO CLEVERLY DONE THAT IT'S ALMOST IMPOSSIBLE FOR A CHILD TO ESCAPE THIS TRAP.

THE PRIEST ASKED CHARLES THESE QUESTIONS.

MY CHILD, WHEN YOU HAVE BEEN GUILTY OF DOING SOMETHING WRONG AT HOME . . . .

WHO WAS THE FIRST TO PUNISH YOU . . .

YOUR FATHER . . . OR YOUR MOTHER?

MY FATHER!

THAT'S RIGHT, MY CHILD.

AS A MATTER OF FACT . . .

THE FATHER IS ALMOST ALWAYS UPSET WITH HIS CHILDREN

AND MORE READY TO SPANK THEM THAN THE MOTHER.

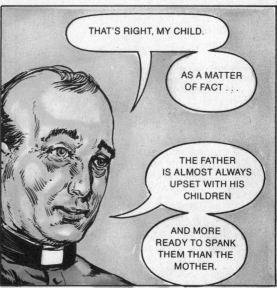

NOW, MY CHILD, TELL US WHO SPANKED YOU THE HARDEST, YOUR FATHER OR YOUR MOTHER?

MY FATHER.

STILL TRUE, MY CHILD.

THE SUPERIOR GOODNESS OF A KIND MOTHER . . .

IS UNDERSTOOD EVEN IN THE ACT OF CORRECTION.

SHE DOESN'T HIT AS HARD AS THE FATHER.

EVEN WHEN YOU DESERVED TO BE SPANKED . . .

DIDN'T *SOMEONE* SOMETIMES COME BETWEEN YOU AND YOUR FATHER'S STICK OR BELT . . . TAKING IT AWAY FROM HIM?

YES, *MANY* TIMES MY MOTHER SAVED ME FROM A REAL HARD SPANKING.

THAT IS SO, MY CHILD. AND NOT ONLY YOU . . . BUT ALL YOUR FRIENDS HERE.

MY CHILDREN, HAVEN'T YOUR GOOD MOTHERS OFTEN SAVED YOU FROM YOUR FATHERS' SPANKINGS?

EVEN WHEN YOU DESERVED IT?

ANSWER ME!

YES, SIR!

YES!

YES, MR. MORIN.

ONE QUESTION MORE . . .

WHEN YOUR FATHER WAS COMING TO WHIP YOU,

DIDN'T YOU THROW YOURSELVES INTO THE ARMS OF SOMEONE TO ESCAPE?

YES, SIR . . . WHEN I WAS GUILTY OF DOING SOMETHING MORE THAN ONCE,

I'D THROW MYSELF INTO MY MOTHER'S ARMS

AS SOON AS I SAW MY FATHER COMING TO WHIP ME.

SHE'D BEG FOR HIM NOT TO HIT ME . . .

AND DID IT SO WELL THAT MANY TIMES I ESCAPED GETTING SPANKED.

NOW THE PRIEST CLOSES THE TRAP. HE USES JESUIT LOGIC TO DRIVE HOME HIS POINT.

YOU HAVE A FATHER AND A MOTHER IN HEAVEN,* DEAR CHILDREN.

YOUR FATHER* IS JESUS, AND YOUR MOTHER* IS MARY.

DON'T FORGET THAT A MOTHER'S HEART IS ALWAYS MORE TENDER,

AND HAS MORE MERCY THAN THAT OF A FATHER.

*THIS IS *NOT* WHAT THE BIBLE SAYS.

MANY TIMES YOU OFFEND YOUR FATHER BY YOUR SINS . . .

YOU MAKE HIM *ANGRY* AGAINST YOU!

DO YOU KNOW WHAT TAKES PLACE IN HEAVEN THEN?

YOUR FATHER IN HEAVEN TAKES HIS ROD TO PUNISH YOU.

HE THREATENS TO *CRUSH* YOU WITH HIS *ROARING THUNDER!*

THE TRAP IS CLOSED AND ROME WILL CONTROL THEIR THINKING ABOUT MARY FOR THE REST OF THEIR LIVES.

AND *THAT* IS HOW THE POPE AND THE PRIESTS OF ROME HAVE ENTIRELY TWISTED AND CHANGED THE GOSPEL. JESUS HAS BECOME SOMEONE THEY ARE AFRAID OF.

IN THE "CHURCH" OF ROME, IT IS NOT JESUS, BUT MARY, WHO REPRESENTS THE INFINITE LOVE AND MERCY OF GOD TO THE SINNER.

THE POOR ROMAN CATHOLICS ARE TOLD IT IS NOT JESUS, BUT MARY,* WHO SAVES THE SINNER.

WHAT A HORRIBLE BLASPHEMY!

*FIFTY YEARS IN THE CHURCH OF ROME, PG. 38

THIS IS HOW SATAN USES ROME TO DESTROY THE SOULS OF THE YOUNG FOREVER . . .

GOD HELP US TO OPEN THEIR EYES THAT IT IS JESUS WHO SAVES.

THE BIBLE CLEARLY STATES:

JESUS SAID: "I AM THE WAY, THE TRUTH, AND THE LIFE: NO MAN COMETH UNTO THE FATHER BUT BY ME."

(JOHN 14:6)

CHINIQUY SAID: FOR THE ROMAN CATHOLIC CHILD, THE DAY OF HIS FIRST COMMUNION IS BOTH BEAUTIFUL AND YET SAD. SO MANY JOYS AND ANXIETIES RISE IN HIS SOUL WHEN FOR THE FIRST TIME HE IS ABOUT TO EAT WHAT HE HAS BEEN TAUGHT TO BELIEVE TO BE HIS GOD.*

*FIFTY YEARS IN THE CHURCH OF ROME, PG. 38-39

THE PRIEST HAD PROMISED US THAT WHAT WE WERE ABOUT TO EAT

WAS THE TRUE BODY, THE TRUE BLOOD AND THE DIVINITY OF JESUS CHRIST.

I WAS ABOUT TO EAT HIM, NOT LIKE A SYMBOL OR A SIGN OR IN MEMORY OF HIM, BUT IN A LITERAL WAY . . . ACTUALLY EAT HIM!

I WAS TO EAT HIS FLESH, HIS BONES, HIS HANDS, HIS FEET, HIS WHOLE BODY.

I HAD TO BELIEVE THIS OR BE CAST INTO HELL FOREVER!!

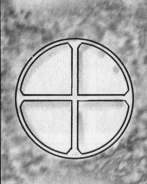

WHILE ALL THE TIME, MY EYES, MY HANDS, MY MOUTH AND MY TONGUE AND MY REASON TOLD ME . . .

THAT WHAT I WAS EATING WAS ONLY A WAFER

THE "CHURCH" OF ROME IS THE MOST SKILLFUL HUMAN MACHINE THE WORLD HAS EVER SEEN.

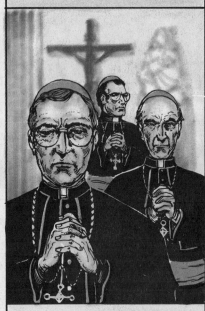

THOSE MEN WHO GUIDE HER IN THE DARK PATHS WHICH SHE FOLLOWS ARE OFTEN MEN OF DEEP THOUGHT.

THEY KNEW VERY WELL THE STRUGGLE WHICH WOULD TAKE PLACE EVEN IN YOUNG MINDS OF CHILDREN AT THE GREAT MOMENT WHEN THEY WOULD BE FORCED TO GIVE UP THEIR COMMON SENSE AND PUT IT INTO THE HANDS OF ROME.

IN ORDER TO PREVENT THESE STRUGGLES WHICH ARE ALWAYS SO DANGEROUS TO THE "CHURCH,"

NOTHING HAD BEEN OVERLOOKED TO DISTRACT THE CHILD'S MIND AND DRAW ATTENTION TO ALL THE EXCITING THINGS GOING ON AROUND THEM.

ALL THIS IS TO GET THEIR MINDS OFF THE COMMUNION ITSELF.

SO THE CHILDREN ARE DRESSED UP AS BEAUTIFULLY AS POSSIBLE.

THE CHURCH IS POMPOUSLY DECORATED. THE CHARMS OF A LOVELY CHOIR AND INSTRUMENTAL MUSIC FORM A PART OF THE PROGRAM.

THE WHOLE PARISH IS INVITED AND THE PEOPLE COME FROM EVERY DIRECTION TO ENJOY THIS MOST BEAUTIFUL SPECTACLE.

PRIESTS FROM NEIGHBORING CHURCHES ARE CALLED TO ADD SOLEMNITY TO THE DAY.

THIS IS RELIGIOUS SHOW BUSINESS AT ITS BEST.

NOW IN THE MIDST OF THAT NEW AND WONDERFUL SPECTACLE OF SINGING LATIN PSALMS, NOT A WORD OF WHICH HE UNDERSTANDS,

IN VIEW OF GOLD AND SILVER ORNAMENTS WHICH GLITTER EVERYWHERE BEFORE HIS DAZZLED EYES, CAN A YOUNG COMMUNICANT THINK FOR A MOMENT OF WHAT HE IS ABOUT TO DO?

WHILE HIS IMAGINATION IS WANDERING FROM ONE SUBJECT TO ANOTHER, THE MOMENT OF COMMUNION ARRIVES . . .

WITHOUT LEAVING HIM TIME TO THINK OF WHAT HE IS ABOUT TO DO. .

HE OPENS HIS MOUTH AND THE PRIEST PUTS UPON HIS TONGUE . . .

A THIN FLAT CAKE OF UNLEAVENED BREAD . . . IT WAS CALLED HIS "WAFER GOD."

IN OTHER WORDS THE WAFER BECAME GOD ALMIGHTY

IT WENT DOWN INTO HIS STOMACH JUST LIKE THE FOOD HE TAKES THREE TIMES A DAY.

THE FIRST FEELING IS SURPRISE AT THE THOUGHT THAT THE CREATOR OF HEAVEN AND EARTH,

THE SAVIOUR OF THE WORLD, COULD SO EASILY PASS DOWN HIS THROAT.

NOW FOLLOW THE CHILDREN HOME AFTER THAT GREAT AND MONSTROUS COMEDY . . . LISTEN TO THEIR CONVERSATIONS AND BURSTS OF LAUGHTER. STUDY THEIR MANNERS, THEIR GLANCES OF SATISFACTION ON THEIR FINE CLOTHES.

NOTICE THE LIGHTNESS OF THEIR ACTIONS AND CONVERSATION IMMEDIATELY AFTER THEIR COMMUNION AND TELL ME IF YOU FIND ANYTHING INDICATING THAT THEY TRUELY BELIEVE IN THE TERRIBLE DOGMA THEY HAVE BEEN TAUGHT.

YOU THINK THAT THEY HONESTLY BELIEVE IN IT? WILL THEY EVER BELIEVE IT WITH THE FIRMNESS OF FAITH WHICH IS ACCOMPANIED BY INTELLIGENCE?

THE POOR CHILD THINKS HE BELIEVES, AND HE SINCERELY TRIES TO DO SO.

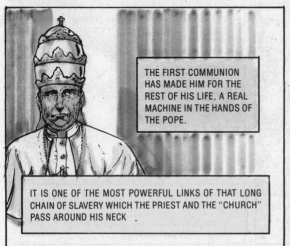

THE FIRST COMMUNION HAS MADE HIM FOR THE REST OF HIS LIFE, A REAL MACHINE IN THE HANDS OF THE POPE.

IT IS ONE OF THE MOST POWERFUL LINKS OF THAT LONG CHAIN OF SLAVERY WHICH THE PRIEST AND THE "CHURCH" PASS AROUND HIS NECK .

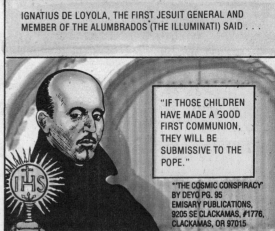

IGNATIUS DE LOYOLA, THE FIRST JESUIT GENERAL AND MEMBER OF THE ALUMBRADOS (THE ILLUMINATI) SAID . . .

"IF THOSE CHILDREN HAVE MADE A GOOD FIRST COMMUNION, THEY WILL BE SUBMISSIVE TO THE POPE."

*"THE COSMIC CONSPIRACY" BY DEYO PG. 95 EMISARY PUBLICATIONS, 9205 SE CLACKAMAS, #1776, CLACKAMAS, OR 97015

"THEY WILL BE IN THE HANDS OF THE SUPREME PONTIFF OF ROME JUST WHAT THE STICK IS IN THE HANDS OF THE TRAVELLER. THEY WILL HAVE NO WILL, NO THOUGHT OF THEIR OWN."

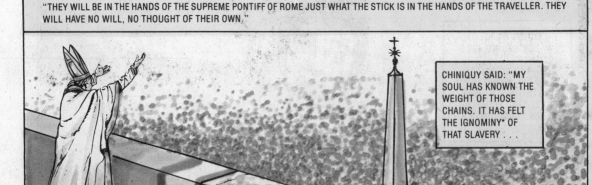

CHINIQUY SAID: "MY SOUL HAS KNOWN THE WEIGHT OF THOSE CHAINS. IT HAS FELT THE IGNOMINY* OF THAT SLAVERY . . .

*SHAME

BUT THE GREAT CONQUEROR OF SOULS (JESUS) HAS CAST DOWN A MERCIFUL EYE ON ME. HE HAS BROKEN MY CHAINS, AND WITH HIS HOLY WORD (THE BIBLE) HE HAS MADE ME FREE."

IN THE ROMAN CATHOLIC COLLEGE, STUDYING FOR THE PRIESTHOOD, CHINIQUY WAS UPSET OVER THE STRANGE THINGS HE LEARNED. A LOT OF IT DIDN'T MAKE SENSE. THE STUDENTS EVEN QUESTIONED IT.

WHAT'S THE DIFFERENCE WITH THE RELIGION OF HEATHEN ROME AND ROME TODAY?

THE ONLY DIFFERENCE IS THE NAMES.

INSTEAD OF CALLING THIS STATUE JUPITER, WE CALL IT PETER.

RIGHT. AND INSTEAD OF CALLING THAT ONE MINERVA OR VENUS, WE CALL IT ST. MARY.

THEY DISCOVERED THE IDOLATRY OF THE PAST WAS STILL WITH THEM, BUT WITH CHRISTIAN NAMES.

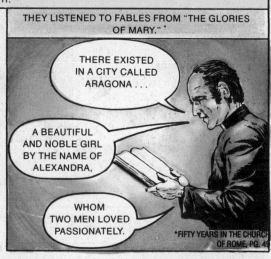

THEY LISTENED TO FABLES FROM "THE GLORIES OF MARY." *

THERE EXISTED IN A CITY CALLED ARAGONA . . .

A BEAUTIFUL AND NOBLE GIRL BY THE NAME OF ALEXANDRA,

WHOM TWO MEN LOVED PASSIONATELY.

*FIFTY YEARS IN THE CHURCH OF ROME, PG. 49

"ONE DAY, MADDENED BY THE JEALOUSY EACH ONE HAD FOR THE OTHER,

THEY FOUGHT TOGETHER, AND BOTH WERE KILLED.

THEIR PARENTS WERE SO MAD AT THE YOUNG GIRL WHO WAS RESPONSIBLE, THAT THEY KILLED HER . . .

. . . CUT OFF HER HEAD AND THREW HER INTO A WELL. A FEW DAYS LATER ST. DOMINIC, PASSING BY THE PLACE, CAME TO THE WELL AND CRIED OUT, 'ALEXANDRA, COME HERE.'

"THE HEAD OF THE GIRL IMMEDIATELY APPEARED ON THE EDGE OF THE WELL AND BEGGED ST. DOMINIC TO HEAR ITS CONFESSION.

HAVING HEARD IT, THE SAINT GAVE HER THE COMMUNION IN THE PRESENCE OF A GREAT MULTITUDE OF PEOPLE.

THEN HE COMMANDED HER TO TELL THEM WHY SHE HAD RECEIVED SO GREAT A FAVOR.

"THOUGH I WAS IN A STATE OF MORTAL SIN WHEN I WAS DECAPITATED, I HAD THE HABIT OF RECITING THE HOLY ROSARY.,

THE VIRGIN PRESERVED MY LIFE.'

THE HEAD, FULL OF LIFE, REMAINED ON THE EDGE OF THE WELL TWO DAYS BEFORE THE EYES OF A GREAT MANY PEOPLE.

AND THEN THE SOUL WENT TO PURGATORY.

BUT 15 DAYS LATER, THE SOUL OF ALEXANDRA APPEARED TO ST. DOMINIC, BRIGHT AND BEAUTIFUL AS A STAR.

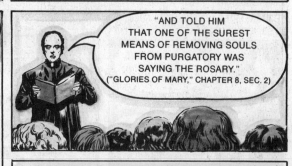

"AND TOLD HIM THAT ONE OF THE SUREST MEANS OF REMOVING SOULS FROM PURGATORY WAS SAYING THE ROSARY." ("GLORIES OF MARY," CHAPTER 8, SEC. 2)

CHINIQUY STUDIED THE WORKS OF HOMER, VIRGIL AND SOCRATES . . . BUT THE BIBLE?

FORBIDDEN BOOKS

HOLY BIBLE

DO NOT TOUCH

HE WAS NOT ALLOWED TO READ IT.

CHINIQUY HAD A PROBLEM IN COLLEGE. HE TOLD HIS INSTRUCTORS WHAT HE BELIEVED, AND MANY TIMES HE GOT IN HOT WATER.

TO GRADUATE AS A PRIEST, PART OF THE OATH WAS TO SAY . . .

"I WILL NEVER INTERPRET THE HOLY SCRIPTURES EXCEPT ACCORDING TO THE UNANIMOUS CONSENT OF THE HOLY FATHERS."

THESE WERE *SOME* OF THE HOLY FATHERS

ST. THOMAS
LIGUORI
BELLARMINE
ST. THOMAS
ST. JEROME
ST. AUGUSTINE

THE ONLY THING ST. JEROME AND ST. AUGUSTINE AGREED ON WAS — THEY DISAGREED ON *EVERY* POINT.

CHINIQUY CHALLENGED HIS INSTRUCTOR ABOUT THIS.

THE WRITINGS OF THE HOLY FATHERS ARE NOWHERE TO BE FOUND . . .

IT'S IMPOSSIBLE TO FIND THEM, TO READ THEM OR TO STUDY THEM.

YOU ARE ONE OF THE MOST LEARNED MEN IN FRANCE . . . AND YOU CAN'T HELP US.

HOW WILL WE EVER KNOW HOW TO PREACH FROM THE BIBLE? THAT OATH STOPS US!

THROUGHOUT HISTORY, THE HOLY FATHERS DISAGREED WITH THE HOLY FATHERS BEFORE THEM.

SOME HOLY FATHERS HAVE DENIED THE SUPREME AUTHORITY OF THE CHURCH . . .

OTHERS HAVE LAUGHED AT THE EX-COMMUNICATIONS OF THE POPES.

IN THE LAST DAYS OF ST. AUGUSTINE, HE SAID REGARDING THIS SCRIPTURE:

"THOU ART PETER AND UPON THIS ROCK, I WILL BUILD MY CHURCH."

ST. AUGUSTINE SAID *CHRIST* WAS THE ROCK!

HE AGREED WITH THE PROTESTANTS!

IT IS YOUR EVIL NATURE THAT MAKES YOU QUESTION THE CHURCH.

CHINIQUY WAS REBUKED AND TOLD TO SUBMIT TO HIS CHURCH OR ELSE.

HE DID BOW TO THE POPE. HE LOST HIS FIGHT AND SURRENDERED HIS REASONING.

WHEN HE BECAME A PRIEST, HE *HAD* TO TAKE THAT OATH.

THIS WOULD KEEP THE PEOPLE FROM THE BIBLE.

THAT NIGHT IN HIS SLEEP, THESE THOUGHTS PLAGUED HIM . . .

YOU REBEL AGAINST THE HOLY GHOST.

YOU DENY THE HOLY SCRIPTURES TO FOLLOW THE STEPS OF SINFUL MEN.

HE CRIED TO HIS WAFER GOD*AND TO THE BLESSED VIRGIN MARY FOR HELP, WITH NO RESPONSE.

HE LAID HIS HEAD ON HIS PILLOW TO SLEEP THE SLEEP OF SPIRITUAL DEATH WITH THE (THEN) TWO HUNDRED MILLION** SLAVES WHOM THE POPE SEES AT HIS FEET.

*SEE PAGE 13
**TODAY IT IS CLOSE TO ONE BILLION.

AS A PRIEST, ONE OF CHINIQUY'S ASSIGNMENTS WAS TO ASSIST THE HIGHLY RESPECTED ARCH PRIEST AT THE PARISH OF ST. CHARLES IN QUEBEC, THE REV. MR. PERRAS, A PIOUS AND LEARNED PRIEST. THIS WAS A GREAT HONOR.

A FEW MONTHS AFTER HE ARRIVED THERE, CHINIQUY HEARD OF TWO SCANDALS THAT MADE HIM VERY UPSET.

MY DEAR CHINIQUY, WHAT'S THE MATTER? PLEASE TELL ME. PERHAPS I CAN HELP.

I'M SAD ABOUT THE FALL OF THE TWO PRIESTS.

I HEARD ABOUT THINGS LIKE THIS IN THE COLLEGE. WHAT WILL HAPPEN TO OUR HOLY CHURCH IN CANADA

IF HER MOST DEVOTED PRIESTS ARE SO WEAK AND HAVE SUCH LITTLE FEAR OF GOD?

MY DEAR YOUNG FRIEND, OUR HOLY CHURCH IS INFALLIBLE.* THE GATES OF HELL CANNOT PREVAIL AGAINST HER.

THE FACT THE HOLY CHURCH KEEPS GOING ON AND ITS INFALLIBILITY* DOES NOT REST ON HUMAN FOUNDATIONS,

OR ON THE PERSONAL HOLINESS OF HER PRIESTS. IT RESTS ON THE PROMISES OF JESUS CHRIST.

*IMPOSSIBLE TO MAKE AN ERROR.

THE SINS AND SCANDALS OF HER PRIESTS WOULD HAVE DESTROYED HER LONG AGO, IF CHRIST WAS NOT IN THE MIDST TO SAVE AND SUSTAIN HER.

THE VERY SINS OF THE PRIESTS MAKE THE SPOTLESS SPOUSE* OF JESUS CHRIST . . .

FLY HIGHER AND HIGHER TOWARDS THE REGIONS OF HOLINESS AS IT IS IN GOD.

*WIFE.

TO BUILD UP CHINIQUY'S FAITH, HE TOLD HIM A STORY TO MAKE HIS POINT.

. YEARS AGO, AN OLD FRIEND OF MINE, BISHOP PLESSIS, TOLD ME THAT HE WAS HEARTBROKEN.

IT SEEMED THAT AFTER TRAVELING OVER HIS HUGE DIOCESE* OF QUEBEC...

. . . HE LEARNED THAT ALL BUT FOUR OF HIS PRIESTS WERE ATHEISTS** AND INFIDELS.***

*TERRITORIAL JURISDICTION OF A BISHOP.
**DIDN'T BELIEVE IN GOD.
***NO LONGER BELIEVED IN THEIR RELIGION.

"BISHOP PLESSIS WEPT AND I REMINDED HIM OF THE HISTORY OF OUR HOLY CHURCH TO GIVE HIM HOPE.

FROM THE 7TH TO THE 15TH CENTURIES, THE CHURCH HAD SEEN DARKER DAYS.

"THEN I TOOK HIM TO THE LIBRARY AND OPENED THE PAGES OF 'THE HISTORY OF THE CHURCH' BY CARDINALS BARONIUS AND FLEURY.

"THEN I SHOWED HIM THE NAMES OF MORE THAN 50 POPES WHO WERE ATHEISTS AND INFIDELS.

YOUR HOLINESS . . . MAY I SPEAK?

"I READ TO HIM ABOUT POPE BORGIA, ALEXANDER VI, WHO PUBLICLY LIVED AS A MARRIED MAN WITH HIS DAUGHTER AND HAD A CHILD BY HER. ROME WAS FILLED WITH MURDER, ADULTERY, AND CRIMES OF EVERY SORT.

"MY DEAR YOUNG FRIEND, WHEN SATAN TRIES TO SHAKE YOUR FAITH BY THE SCANDALS YOU SEE

THEN, REMEMBER POPE STEPHEN. AFTER FIGHTING WITH HIS ENEMY, POPE CONSTANTINE II . . .

PUT OUT HIS EYES AND CONDEMNED HIM TO DIE.

GULP

REMEMBER THE POPE WHO DUG UP THE BODY OF HIS PREDECESSOR AND TOOK IT TO COURT; WHEN THE DEAD POPE WAS FOUND GUILTY OF COMMITTING HORRIBLE CRIMES,

THEY CUT OFF ITS HEAD AND DRAGGED THE BODY THROUGH THE MUDDY STREETS OF ROME AND THREW IT INTO THE TIBER RIVER.*

*"FIFTY YEARS IN THE 'CHURCH' OF ROME," PGS. 86-87

"YES, CHINIQUY, WHEN YOUR MIND IS OPPRESSED BY THE SECRET CRIMES OF PRIESTS, REMEMBER THAT 12 POPES HAVE BEEN RAISED TO THAT HIGH AND HOLY DIGNITY . . .

BY THE INFLUENCE OF THE RICH AND INFLUENTIAL PROSTITUTES OF ROME.

"REMEMBER THAT YOUNG ILLEGITIMATE JOHN XI, THE SON OF POPE SERGIUS, WHO WAS MADE A POPE WHEN HE WAS ONLY 12 YEARS OLD . . .

BY THE INFLUENCE OF HIS PROSTITUTE MOTHER, MAROSIA. BUT HE BECAME SO HORRIBLY DEPRAVED SEXUALLY THAT HE WAS THROWN OFF THE PAPAL THRONE BY THE PEOPLE OF ROME.

IF OUR HOLY CHURCH HAS BEEN ABLE TO PASS THROUGH SUCH STORMS WITHOUT PERISHING, IT IS THE LIVING PROOF THAT CHRIST IS HER PILOT,

THAT SHE IS IMPERISHABLE AND INFALLIBLE BECAUSE ST. PETER IS HER FOUNDATION!"

THE LECTURE LASTED FOR HOURS. HE SPOKE OF THOSE UNMENTIONABLE CRIMES OF SO MANY POPES TO STRENGTHEN CHINIQUY'S FAITH.

BUT IT ALMOST DESTROYED THE YOUNG PRIEST.

IN ONE OF HIS OATHS, CHINIQUY PROMISED NEVER TO LISTEN TO THE VOICE OF HIS CONSCIENCE, OR MAKE A PRIVATE JUDGMENT THAT OPPOSED THE TEACHING OF HIS CHURCH.

THESE SCRIPTURES WENT THROUGH HIS MIND.

IT DOESN'T MAKE SENSE.

BY THEIR FRUITS YE SHALL KNOW THEM.*

A GOOD TREE CANNOT BRING FORTH EVIL FRUIT.**

*MATT. 7:20
**MATT. 7:18

HAS THE CHURCH SYSTEM OF ROME CHANGED? ONLY ON THE SURFACE!

IT IS STILL THE MOTHER OF HARLOTS OF REV. 17, AND JESUS CHRIST WILL JUDGE HER FOR HER CRIMES.

PRIESTS ALWAYS LAUGHED AT PROTESTANTS BECAUSE THEY CLAIMED ROME NEVER CHANGED. BUT IN CHINIQUY'S LIFETIME, POPE PIUS IX DID SOMETHING THAT CLOSED THEIR MOUTHS.

STORMS AND FIGHTS RAGED AMONG ROMAN CATHOLICS ABOUT MARY'S OWN BIRTH BEING WITHOUT SIN.

NO!

LIES!

I SAID THE HOLY SPIRIT CAME UPON MARY'S MOTHER AND THE VIRGIN MARY WAS BORN WITHOUT SIN.

IT'S TRUE!

THIS CONTROVERSY WAS A BIG ISSUE. POPE AFTER POPE HAD AVOIDED IT UNTIL PIUS IX HAD A DREAM IN WHICH HE WAS TOLD IF THE IMMACULATE CONCEPTION BECAME DOGMA, IT WOULD END ALL THE CHURCH'S PROBLEMS.

ON DEC. 8, 1854, WITH A CROWN ON HIS HEAD AND MORE THAN 50,000 PEOPLE AT HIS FEET, THIS HISTORIC EVENT TOOK PLACE.

HOLY FATHER, TELL US IF WE CAN BELIEVE AND TEACH . . .

THAT THE MOTHER OF GOD, THE HOLY VIRGIN WAS IMMACULATE* IN HER CONCEPTION.

I DO NOT KNOW. LET US ASK THE LIGHT OF THE HOLY GHOST.

*WITHOUT SIN.

THE QUESTION WAS ASKED A THIRD TIME. THEN THE POPE ANSWERED.

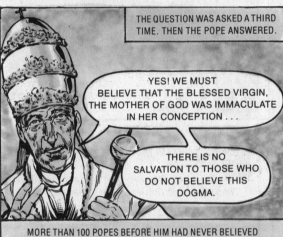

YES! WE MUST BELIEVE THAT THE BLESSED VIRGIN, THE MOTHER OF GOD WAS IMMACULATE IN HER CONCEPTION . . .

THERE IS NO SALVATION TO THOSE WHO DO NOT BELIEVE THIS DOGMA.

MORE THAN 100 POPES BEFORE HIM HAD NEVER BELIEVED IT. THE HOLY FATHERS NEVER BELIEVED IT. BUT NOW IT WAS IN EFFECT AS A DIVINE DECREE.

HOW COULD CHINIQUY EXPLAIN THIS, KNOWING THAT FOR THE LAST 10 CENTURIES, WHEN QUESTIONED ABOUT THIS SUBJECT, THE OFFICIAL POSITION OF HIS CHURCH WAS, "I DON'T KNOW."

THE "CHURCH" *NEVER* MAKES MISTAKES BECAUSE SHE IS INFALLIBLE . . . BUT ON DEC. 8, 1854, POPE PIUS IX SAID, "THE CHURCH HAS ALWAYS KNOWN AND BELIEVED THE VIRGIN MARY WAS IMMACULATE."

THIS ANNOUNCEMENT STUNNED ROMAN CATHOLICS ALL OVER THE WORLD.

A FARMER ASKED CHINIQUY THIS QUESTION.

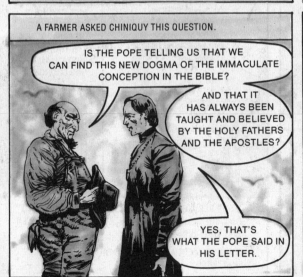

IS THE POPE TELLING US THAT WE CAN FIND THIS NEW DOGMA OF THE IMMACULATE CONCEPTION IN THE BIBLE?

AND THAT IT HAS ALWAYS BEEN TAUGHT AND BELIEVED BY THE HOLY FATHERS AND THE APOSTLES?

YES, THAT'S WHAT THE POPE SAID IN HIS LETTER.

BUT THE BIBLE SAYS, "ALL HAVE SINNED AND COME SHORT OF THE GLORY OF GOD"* . . . AND "THERE IS NONE RIGHTEOUS, NO, NOT ONE."**

ALL INCLUDES MARY.

HUMPH!

*ROM. 3:23, **ROM. 3:10

THE FARMER WONDERED . . . IF *THIS* NEW DOGMA WAS NOT IN THE BIBLE, THEN WHAT ABOUT PURGATORY AND CONFESSION?

CHINIQUY WAS EMBARRASSED AND ASHAMED. HE PRAYED THAT NIGHT AND AGAIN THE VOICE OF GOD CALLED TO HIM THROUGH THESE SCRIPTURES . . . "COME OUT" OF BABYLON.*

BUT CHINIQUY STAYED IN HIS DARK DUNGEON OF ERROR.

*REV. 18:4

WHEN CHINIQUY WAS A PRIEST, HE PREACHED A SERMON ON "THE VIRGIN MARY'S POWER IN HEAVEN."

WHO AMONG YOU CAN REFUSE A REQUEST MADE BY YOUR MOTHER?

WHO WILL BREAK OR SADDEN HER LOVING HEART WHEN SHE WEEPS . . .

AND ASKS FOR YOU TO HELP HER WHEN IT IS IN YOUR POWER TO DO IT?

IF MY BELOVED MOTHER WERE LIVING, AND SHE ASKED ME **ANY** FAVOR WHICH WAS IN MY POWER TO DO SO . . .

I'D PREFER TO CRUSH MY HAND AND HAVE IT BURNED TO CINDERS THAN TO SAY NO TO HER.

THE LOVE FOR HIS MOTHER, RESPECT AND OBEDIENCE . . .

WERE PRACTICED TO PERFECTION BY JESUS CHRIST, THE SON OF GOD, AND SON OF MARY.

IN HEAVEN HE **STILL** MAKES SUBMISSION TO THE WILL OF HIS MOTHER.

THE PEOPLE WERE MOVED TO TEARS. HE TOLD OF JESUS' ANGER OVER OUR SINS. HOW CAN WE **DARE** TO LOOK AT HIM? INSTEAD, WE LOOK TO MARY FOR OUR HELP.

TO QUOTE HIS HOLINESS POPE GREGORY THE 16TH HE SAID. . .

. . .IN THE MOST SOLEMN MANNER, THAT **MARY** IS THE ONLY HOPE FOR SINNERS.

JESUS **CANNOT** REFUSE ANY REQUEST FROM THE QUEEN OF HEAVEN.

LET US GO TO HER TO PLEAD OUR CAUSE, AND SHE WILL ANSWER.

EVERYBODY LOVED THAT MESSAGE. THE PEOPLE, AND EVEN THE BISHOP, CONGRATULATED CHINIQUY.

WHAT'S THIS???

THAT NIGHT, CHINIQUY OPENED HIS BIBLE AND READ SOMETHING THAT MADE HIM START SWEATING . . . HIS HEART SPEEDED UP.

WHAT HE READ TORE HIS MESSAGE TO SHREDS! HE HAD **LIED** TO HIS PEOPLE!

HE FOUND WHEN JESUS WAS A CHILD, HE OBEYED HIS MOTHER,

BUT IN HIS PUBLIC MINISTRY, EACH TIME MARY ASKED FOR A FAVOR, JESUS WOULD REBUKE HER.

JESUS LOVED MARY, BUT HE COULD SEE AHEAD HOW THE ROMAN CATHOLICS WOULD SET UP MARY WORSHIP. ONLY BY REFUSING HER IN PUBLIC, COULD JESUS SHOW THE WORLD HE WAS AGAINST PRAYING TO MARY.

CHINIQUY CHECKED THE OTHER GOSPELS . . THEY SAID THE SAME THING.

HE FELT LIKE A SWORD HAD GONE THROUGH HIM. HIS FAITH WAS SHAKEN. EVERYTHING HE HAD PREACHED THAT DAY WAS A LIE.

O MY GOD, WHAT HAVE I DONE?

LUKE 8:19-21 MATT. 12:46-50
MARK 3:32-35 JOHN 2:1-5

IT WAS LIKE A VOICE SAYING TO HIM, "HOW DARE YOU PREACH THIS WITH YOUR APOSTATE AND LYING CHURCH . . .

THAT JESUS ALWAYS GRANTED ALL THE PETITIONS OF MARY,

WHEN THE WORD OF GOD SAYS IT ISN'T TRUE!"

JESUS REBUKED MARY TO MAKE PEOPLE UNDERSTAND THAT SHE COULD **NEVER** BE AN INTERCESSOR* BETWEEN MAN AND CHRIST.

CHINIQUY WEPT ALL NIGHT. HIS FAITH IN MARY WAS SHATTERED.

*1 TIM. 2:5

THE NEXT MORNING, CHINIQUY LOOKED SO BAD, BISHOP PRINCE ASKED IF HE COULD HELP HIM. CHINIQUY EXPLAINED WHAT HAPPENED. THE BISHOP WAS CONFUSED. CHINIQUY ASKED HIM THE FOLLOWING QUESTIONS:

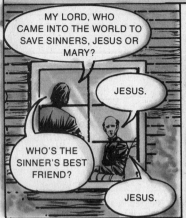

MY LORD, WHO CAME INTO THE WORLD TO SAVE SINNERS, JESUS OR MARY?

JESUS.

WHO'S THE SINNER'S BEST FRIEND?

JESUS.

WHEN MARY AND JESUS WERE ON EARTH . .

DID JESUS INVITE SINNERS TO COME TO HIMSELF OR TO MARY FOR THEIR SALVATION?

TO HIMSELF.

DOES THE BIBLE SHOW ANYWHERE A SINNER AFRAID TO GO TO JESUS,

AND IN TURN, ASKS MARY TO APPROACH JESUS TO HELP HIM OUT?

NO, I DON'T REMEMBER SUCH A THING.

THE THIEF ON THE CROSS NEXT TO JESUS . . . DID HE DO WELL TO TALK TO JESUS OR TO MARY, STANDING AT HIS FEET?

TO JESUS, OF COURSE.

IF JESUS LOVED SINNERS MORE THAN MARY DID WHEN HE WAS ON THE EARTH, AND HE WAS MORE THEIR TRUE FRIEND THAN SHE WAS . . .

AND IF JESUS TOOK MORE INTEREST IN THEIR BEING SAVED THAN MARY DID,

AND IF IT'S BETTER TO GO TO JESUS THAN TO MARY TO GET SAVED . . .

AND SINCE JESUS IS UP IN HEAVEN NOW . . .

HAS HE LOST ANY OF THAT SUPERIOR, DIVINE LOVE AND MERCY THAT HE HAD FOR LOST SINNERS?

THE BISHOP ANSWERED . . . NO!

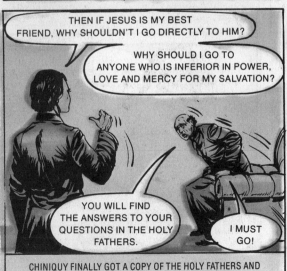

THEN IF JESUS IS MY BEST FRIEND, WHY SHOULDN'T I GO DIRECTLY TO HIM?

WHY SHOULD I GO TO ANYONE WHO IS INFERIOR IN POWER, LOVE AND MERCY FOR MY SALVATION?

YOU WILL FIND THE ANSWERS TO YOUR QUESTIONS IN THE HOLY FATHERS.

I MUST GO!

CHINIQUY FINALLY GOT A COPY OF THE HOLY FATHERS AND DISCOVERED THAT FOR THE FIRST 600 YEARS, THE WORSHIP OF MARY WAS NEVER PUSHED OR TAUGHT BY THE HOLY FATHERS.

ALL OF HIS TEXT BOOKS IN COLLEGE QUOTING THE HOLY FATHERS THAT SAID THEY BELIEVED IN MARY WORSHIP WERE OUTRIGHT FORGERIES AND LIES.

GOD WAS STILL CALLING TO CHINIQUY TO COME OUT OF BABYLON. (REV. 18:4)

GOD . . . WHERE CAN I GO?

POOR CHINIQUY STILL DID NOT KNOW THE LOVING JESUS.

HIS HOPE WAS STILL IN THE ROMAN CATHOLIC SYSTEM.

21

IN 1834, CHINIQUY WAS A PRIEST, AND THEY GAVE HIM A JOB NOBODY WANTED . . . FIRST CHAPLAIN OF THE QUEBEC MARINE HOSPITAL. SAILORS WERE COMING IN WITH SMALLPOX AND CHOLERA. HIS JOB WAS TO ADMINISTER SPIRITUAL COMFORT AND LAST RITES BEFORE THEY DIED.

BEFORE FACING THESE PATIENTS, CHINIQUY DRANK A GLASS OF BRANDY. IN THOSE DAYS MANY PEOPLE BELIEVED IT WOULD PROTECT THEM FROM DEADLY GERMS, BECAUSE ALCOHOL WAS A PRESERVATIVE.

WHAT ARE YOU DOING THERE?

WHAT YOU JUST DRANK WAS POISON.

DR. DOUGLAS, WHO WAS ONE OF THE BEST SURGEONS IN QUEBEC, WAS UPSET WHEN HE SAW CHINIQUY DRINK BRANDY. CHINIQUY LAUGHED AT HIM BECAUSE HE KNEW DR. DOUGLAS WAS A PROTESTANT AND WAS AGAINST LIQUOR.

HE TRIED TO EXPLAIN WHAT ALCOHOL DID TO THE HUMAN BODY, BUT CHINIQUY WOULDN'T BELIEVE IT.

TOMORROW MORNING, THERE WILL BE AN AUTOPSY OF A SAILOR WHO JUST DIED.

I WANT YOU TO SEE WITH YOUR OWN EYES WHAT ALCOHOL DOES TO THE HUMAN BODY.

CHINIQUY WAS INTERESTED IN ANATOMY AND HE AGREED TO JOIN DR. DOUGLAS TO WATCH THE AUTOPSY.

GOD USED THIS STRANGE MEETING TO OPEN UP A NEW WORLD FOR CHINIQUY THAT WOULD DESTROY THE LIQUOR INDUSTRY IN CANADA.

I HAVE NO DOUBT THAT THIS MAN WAS INSTANTLY KILLED BY A GLASS OF RUM HE DRANK ONE HOUR BEFORE HE DIED.

HE LET CHINIQUY EXAMINE THE BLOOD VEINS WITH A POWERFUL MICROSCOPE AND THIS IS WHAT HE SAW: THAT RUM CAUSED A RUPTURE IN THE AORTA* THAT CARRIES THE BLOOD FROM THE HEART. IT BROKE LIKE A DAM, AND KILLED HIM.

*ARTERY

HE SAW THOUSANDS OF LITTLE HOLES (PERFORATIONS) IN THE WALLS OF THE BLOOD VESSELS IN THE ESOPHAGUS AND STOMACH.

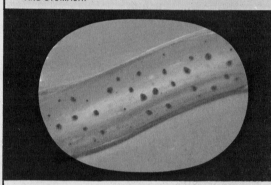

ALCOHOL CAUSED THE BLOOD TO LEAK OUT OF ITS NORMAL PASSAGEWAYS INTO THE BODY.

YOU SEE, CHINIQUY, ALCOHOL *IS* PURE POISON. IT WEAKENS THE NERVES AND MUSCLES.

DR. DOUGLAS TOLD HIM HOW EVERY PART OF THE BODY FIGHTS TO KEEP ALCOHOL FROM COMING INTO ITS TERRITORY, AND HOW THE ORGANS OF THE BODY ARE DESTROYED BECAUSE OF IT.

THE ABOVE WERE THE MEDICAL VIEWS OF SOME DOCTORS IN 1834

IT IS A TERRIBLE WAR THAT GOES ON.

EVERYWHERE ALCOHOL GOES INTO THE BODY, IT LEAVES SCARS AND TERRIBLE DAMAGE.

THE BIBLE SAYS, "WINE IS A MOCKER." (PROV. 20:1) "AT THE LAST IT BITETH LIKE A SERPENT, AND IT STINGETH LIKE AN ADDER (A POISONOUS SNAKE)." (PROV. 23:32)

ALCOHOL HAS KILLED MORE MEN THAN ANY OTHER POISON.

CHINIQUY SAW OVER 100 AUTOPSIES. THEY ALL TOLD THE SAME STORY.

EVEN WITH ALL THIS EVIDENCE, CHINIQUY WOULD NOT GIVE UP HIS BRANDY AND WINE.

A BEAUTIFUL YOUNG LADY WHO CAME TO CHINIQUY'S CONFESSIONAL BELONGED TO ONE OF THE MOST RESPECTABLE FAMILIES IN QUEBEC. SHE HAD A PROBLEM. THE HORRIBLE TRUE STORY YOU ARE ABOUT TO READ IS THE THING THAT MADE CHINIQUY SWEAR THAT HE WOULD *NEVER* TOUCH LIQUOR AGAIN.

THIS YOUNG LADY'S MOTHER HAD ENCOURAGED HER TO DRINK WINE SOCIALLY, AND THE GIRL BECAME HOOKED.

SHE TRIED TO STOP DRINKING, BUT SHE COULDN'T . . . THE ALCOHOL WAS NOW CONTROLLING HER.

SHE HAD ONE OF THE MOST BEAUTIFUL BABIES CHINIQUY HAD EVER SEEN.

HER NAME WAS LUCY. SHE WAS AN ANGEL, AND HER MOTHER LOVED HER, KISSING HER CONSTANTLY, HOLDING LUCY NEXT TO HER HEART.

FATHER CHINIQUY, WE HAVE EVERYTHING . . LITTLE LUCY, A BEAUTIFUL HOME, BUT MY WIFE CAN'T STOP DRINKING!

HER HUSBAND EXPLAINED HOW THEIR DOCTOR HAD PRESCRIBED WINE FOR HIS WIFE. IT WAS NOW A HORRIBLE PROBLEM. HE BEGGED CHINIQUY FOR HELP. NO ONE KNEW HIS TERRIBLE SECRET.

ONE DAY, CHINIQUY WAS CALLED TO THEIR HOME.

IT'S HORRIBLE, FATHER. LITTLE LUCY IS DEAD! AND HER MOTHER IS TRYING TO COMMIT SUICIDE!

THEY NEED YOUR HELP!

WITHIN MINUTES THEY GOT THERE.

CHINIQUY COULD NOT BELIEVE HIS EYES.

THE YOUNG LADY WAS TEARING HER ROBE TO SHREDS . . . TEARING OUT HER HAIR AND CUTTING HER FACE WITH HER FINGERNAILS.

OH, FOR GOD'S SAKE, GIVE ME A KNIFE SO I CAN CUT MY THROAT!

I AM THE MURDERESS OF MY OWN DEAR LUCY!

I KILLED MY CHILD! MY DARLING IS DEAD!

MY HANDS ARE RED WITH HER BLOOD. OH, THAT I MAY DIE WITH HER.

OH, DEAR FATHER CHINIQUY, FOR GOD'S SAKE, GIVE ME A KNIFE SO I CAN CUT MY THROAT!!

SHE TOLD HOW SHE WAS DRUNK AND WHILE HOLDING HER PRECIOUS LITTLE LUCY IN HER ARMS, SHE FELL. LITTLE LUCY'S HEAD STRUCK THE SHARP CORNER OF THE STOVE. HER BRAINS AND BLOOD SPREAD ON THE FLOOR. SHE SCREAMED, "MY CHILD IS DEAD! I HAVE KILLED HER! CURSED LIQUOR! . . . CURSED WINE . . . I AM DAMNED! . . . CURSED DRINK?"

CHINIQUY WENT INTO THE NEXT ROOM AND SAW THE ONCE BEAUTIFUL CHILD. LITTLE LUCY WAS DEAD. HER FACE WAS COVERED WITH HER BLOOD AND BRAINS. THE STOVE HAD UPSET ON THE FLOOR, AND THE AWFUL DEATH OF HER CHILD HAD BROUGHT THE MOTHER BACK TO HER SENSES. SHE WAS NOW COLD SOBER.

PLEASE, FATHER CHINIQUY, IN THE NAME OF GOD, SPEND THE NIGHT WITH US.

PLEASE KEEP ALL THIS A SECRET. PLEASE HELP US.

FOR HOURS, SHE CRIED. IT WAS A NIGHTMARE AS SHE TOLD THE GRUESOME STORY OVER AND OVER AGAIN.

I CAN'T LIVE A DAY LONGER.

OH, THAT I COULD BE BURIED IN THE SAME GRAVE WITH HER!

IT TOOK 4 MEN TO HOLD HER. AT ABOUT 10 P.M., SHE OVERPOWERED THEM ALL, BROKE AWAY, AND RAN TO WHERE LITTLY LUCY WAS.

SHE RIPPED THE BANDAGE OFF HER LITTLE GIRL'S HEAD AND KISSED THE WOUND. SHE HELD HER BABY AND RAN AROUND THE ROOM LIKE A PHANTOM.

GIVE ME A KISS, LUCY. YOUR LIPS ARE COLD.

CAN YOU ASK THE BLESSED VIRGIN TO PRAY FOR ME? AH, NO . . . I AM DAMNED FOREVER.

THE MOTHER AND CHILD WERE COVERED WITH BLOOD. AT 11 P.M., ON HER KNEES, HOLDING LUCY, SHE SAID TO CHINIQUY.

DEAR FATHER CHINIQUY, WHY DIDN'T I FOLLOW YOUR ADVICE? YOU TRIED SO OFTEN TO MAKE ME GIVE UP THOSE CURSED INTOXICATING WINES!

HOW MANY TIMES YOU SAID, "WINE IS A MOCKER AND STINGS LIKE A SNAKE!" HOW MANY TIMES YOU ASKED ME IN THE NAME OF MY CHILD, MY DEAR HUSBAND, AND IN THE NAME OF GOD, TO GIVE UP THE USE OF THOSE CURSED DRINKS?

*PROVERBS 20:1 AND PROVERBS 23:32

BUT NOW, LISTEN TO MY PRAYER . . .

GO ALL OVER CANADA. TELL ALL THE FATHERS **NEVER** TO PUT ANY INTOXICATING DRINKS BEFORE THE EYES OF THEIR CHILDREN . . .

IT WAS AT MY FATHER'S TABLE THAT I FIRST LEARNED TO DRINK THAT WINE WHICH I WILL CURSE DURING ALL ETERNITY.

TELL ALL THOSE MOTHERS **NEVER** TO TASTE THESE ABOMINABLE DRINKS. IT WAS MY MOTHER WHO FIRST TAUGHT ME TO DRINK THAT WINE WHICH I WILL CURSE AS LONG AS GOD IS!

TAKE THE BLOOD OF MY CHILD AND GO REDDEN WITH IT THE TOP OF THE DOORS OF EVERY HOUSE IN CANADA,

AND SAY TO ALL THOSE WHO DWELL IN THOSE HOUSES THAT THE BLOOD WAS SHED BY THE HAND OF A MURDERESS MOTHER WHEN SHE WAS DRUNK.

WITH THAT BLOOD, WRITE ON THE WALLS OF EVERY HOUSE IN CANADA THAT 'WINE IS A MOCKER.

TELL THE FRENCH CANADIANS HOW, ON THE DEAD BODY OF MY CHILD, I HAVE CURSED THAT WINE WHICH HAS MADE ME SO WRETCHEDLY MISERABLE AND GUILTY.

SHE PAUSED FOR A MOMENT AND SAID . . .

IN THE NAME OF GOD, TELL ME, CAN MY CHILD FORGIVE ME HER DEATH?

CAN SHE ASK GOD TO LOOK ON ME WITH MERCY?

CAN SHE CAUSE THE BLESSED VIRGIN MARY TO PRAY FOR ME AND OBTAIN MY PARDON?

THEN SHE SCREAMED:

I AM LOST! WHEN I WAS DRUNK, I KILLED MY CHILD! CURSED WINE!

SHE FELL TO THE FLOOR, A CORPSE. TORRENTS OF BLOOD WERE FLOWING FROM HER MOUTH ON HER DEAD CHILD, WHICH SHE HELD TO HER BREAST.

THE CORONER'S VERDICT WAS: THE CHILD'S DEATH WAS ACCIDENTAL. THE DISTRESSED MOTHER DIED 6 HOURS LATER WITH A BROKEN HEART.

TWO DAYS LATER THE MOTHER WAS BURIED WITH LITTLE LUCY CLASPED IN HER ARMS.

CHINIQUY GOT ALONE WITH GOD. TWO NIGHTS LATER, WHILE IN CONSTANT PRAYER, HE MADE THIS OATH:

FOR MY DEAR SAVIOR JESUS' SAKE AND FOR THE GOOD OF MY COUNTRY . . .

O MY GOD, I PROMISE THAT I WILL **NEVER** AGAIN DRINK INTOXICATING DRINKS.

I WILL, MOREOVER, DO ALL IN MY POWER . . .

TO PERSUADE THE OTHER PRIESTS AND PEOPLE . . .

TO MAKE THE SAME SACRIFICE.

DURING THE NEXT TWO YEARS, HE WAS THE ONLY PRIEST IN CANADA WHO WOULD NOT DRINK.

ALL THE OTHER PRIESTS TURNED ON HIM. HE GOT INSULTS, SNEERS, AND REBUKES EVERYWHERE HE WENT.

TO SHOW THEIR HATE FOR HIM, HIS BISHOP TRANSFERRED HIM TO THE LAST PLACE HE WANTED TO GO.

IN 1838, HE WAS SENT TO BEAUPORT, QUEBEC. ALMOST EVERYONE IN THE PARISH WAS A DRUNKARD.

THE SALOON KEEPERS IN BEAUPORT WERE RICH, AND THE PEOPLE WERE IN RAGS.

THEY FOUGHT LIKE DOGS IN THE STREETS.

THEY HATED CHINIQUY FOR COMING THERE.

THE OTHER PRIESTS WANTED CHINIQUY TO FALL FLAT ON HIS FACE.

BUT CHINIQUY'S LOVE FOR HIS PEOPLE SOON WON THEIR HEARTS.

YOU ALL KNOW THE MISERY AND SIN THAT ALCOHOL HAS CAUSED IN YOUR LIVES AND YOUR CHILDREN'S.

HIS BLAZING SERMONS AGAINST LIQUOR STARTED A FIRE. THE PEOPLE LISTENED AND WEPT, AND MADE A STAND AGAINST LIQUOR.

THEIR TOWN WAS HEALED.

HIS FELLOW PRIESTS WERE OUTRAGED!

THE CHURCHES ALL OVER CANADA WERE JAMMED, TO HEAR HIM.

FIRST HE'D FIND OUT HOW MUCH DAMAGE LIQUOR HAD CAUSED THEIR TOWN IN THE PAST 20 YEARS. THEN HE'D LET THEM HAVE IT FROM THE PULPIT.

YOU REMEMBER THE 7 YOUNG MOTHERS WHO DIED OF D.T.'S?*

AND THE ONE WHO HUNG HERSELF? AND ALL THE STARVING CHILDREN DESTROYED BECAUSE THEIR DRUNKEN PARENTS COULDN'T TAKE CARE OF THEM?

DO YOU KNOW HOW MUCH MONEY YOU SPENT ON LIQUOR IN 15 YEARS? OVER 100,000 DOLLARS!

CHINIQUY WOULD WEEP WITH THE PEOPLE. HUNDREDS OF ROMAN CATHOLIC FAMILIES TOOK THE PLEDGE TO STOP DRINKING.

MOTHERS WHO HAD BEEN BEATEN BY THEIR DRUNKEN HUSBANDS AND FATHERS, BLESSED THE DAY CHINIQUY CAME AMONG THEM. THEIR HOMES WERE SAVED.

*DELIRIUM TREMENS — HALLUCINATIONS WITH TREMORS, CAUSED BY PROLONGED USE OF ALCOHOLIC LIQUORS.

DR. DOUGLAS SEPARATED THE ALCOHOL OUT OF THE LIQUOR AND GAVE IT TO THE DOGS AND CATS.

AND THE PEOPLE SAW THE ANIMALS DIE BEFORE THEIR EYES.

NOW, DO YOU UNDERSTAND?

TEMPERANCE (FIGHT AGAINST LIQUOR) WAS SWEEPING CANADA LIKE A PRAIRIE FIRE.

MEN AND WOMEN SWORE OFF LIQUOR . . . SALOONS WERE CLOSED.

ROMAN CATHOLICS WERE REGAINING THEIR SELF-RESPECT. HOMES WERE HEALED, AND CHINIQUY BECAME THE MOST LOVED PRIEST IN CANADA.

HE WENT TO HIS PEOPLE IN KAMOURASKA, HIS HOME TOWN, AND THEY TOOK THE PLEDGE.

IN 4 YEARS, 200,000 PEOPLE PROMISED TO STOP DRINKING, AND THEY MEANT IT.

HIS DEADLIEST ENEMIES WERE HIS FELLOW PRIESTS AND BISHOPS.

HE'S ACTING LIKE A PROTESTANT.

WE MUST STOP HIM.

TEMPERANCE WAS GAINING MOMENTUM, AND THEY COULDN'T STOP HIM, OR IT.

BREWERIES SHUT DOWN. MERCHANTS WOULD BRING THEIR BARRELS OF LIQUOR TO THE TOWN SQUARE AND CHINIQUY WOULD SET THEM ON FIRE.

HOORAY!

HOORAY

IT WAS FULL SCALE WAR AGAINST LIQUOR, AND CHINIQUY WON. IN JUNE, 1850, LIQUOR WAS OUTLAWED IN CANADA, AND IT BECAME THE LAW OF THE LAND.

PEOPLE HEAPED PRAISES ON CHINIQUY'S HEAD, WHICH UPSET HIM. HE WANTED GOD TO GET THE HONOR. HE WAS OFFICIALLY CALLED THE "APOSTLE OF TEMPERANCE OF CANADA."

THE MORE THEY PRAISED HIM AND GAVE HIM GIFTS OF MONEY, THE WORSE HE FELT.

BECAUSE OF HIS POPULARITY WITH THE PEOPLE, CHINIQUY'S ENEMIES IN THE INSTITUTION OF ROME KEPT GROWING . . .

THEY WERE FILLED WITH JEALOUSY.

BOTH ROMAN CATHOLICS AND PROTESTANTS ALIKE LOVED HIM. HE BECAME THE HERO OF CANADA.

MY HUSBAND DOESN'T BEAT ME ANYMORE.

PRAISE GOD FOR THAT GOOD NEWS.

I'VE BEEN SOBER FOR 3 YEARS NOW.

NOW WE CAN SAVE MONEY. WE THANK GOD FOR YOU, FATHER CHINIQUY. WE'LL PAY OFF OUR FARM.

GOD HAD USED THIS MAN IN A MARVELLOUS WAY TO HEAL CANADA OF THAT HORRIBLE CURSE. UNKNOWN TO CHINIQUY, THERE WAS ANOTHER MAN WHO TOOK THE PLEDGE AGAINST LIQUOR IN THE UNITED STATES, WHO ALSO LOVED CHINIQUY. HIS NAME WAS ABRAHAM LINCOLN. (SEE "PORTRAIT LIFE OF LINCOLN", PG. 144 & 149)

ON DEC. 15, 1850, CHINIQUY RECEIVED A LETTER FROM THE BISHOP OF CHICAGO, ILLINOIS.

THE BISHOP TOLD OF RICH AND FERTILE LANDS IN THE STATE OF ILLINOIS AND THE MISSISSIPPI VALLEY THAT THE CATHOLIC CHURCH WANTED.

THEY BELIEVED IT WOULD BECOME THE BREAD BASKET OF THE WORLD . . . AND THOSE WHO CONTROLLED IT COULD BECOME THE RULERS OF THE UNITED STATES.

THIS WOULD BE DONE QUIETLY. HE SHARED HIS PLAN WITH CHINIQUY.

CATHOLIC EMIGRANTS WERE POURING INTO THE UNITED STATES.

BUT THEY **MUST** BE DIRECTED WHERE TO SETTLE. IF THEY GOT NEAR PROTESTANTS, THEY COULD BE SWALLOWED UP.

ROME WANTED THEM TO COME TO MISSOURI, IOWA, KANSAS, ETC., WHILE THE LAND WAS STILL CHEAP.

WITH THEIR EXPLODING FAMILIES, WEALTH AND UNITY, THEY COULD RULE EVERYTHING.

THE BISHOP BEGGED CHINIQUY TO LEAD THE ROMAN CATHOLIC FRENCH CANADIAN FARMERS DOWN TO ILLINOIS TO TAKE THE LAND.

CHICAGO — 2 WEEKS LATER.

CHINIQUY WILL DO IT! HE'S COMING TO ILLINOIS!

HE WANTS TO SPEND THE REST OF HIS LIFE

EXTENDING THE POWER AND INFLUENCE OF ROME

OVER THE UNITED STATES!

IN JUNE OF 1851, CHINIQUY ARRIVED IN CHICAGO. ITS POPULATION WAS 30,000 PEOPLE.

THE BISHOP LIVES IN THERE, FATHER.

HE HAD DINNER WITH THE BISHOP WHO LIVED IN A MISERABLE HOUSE WITH PLANKS ON THE FLOOR.

BISHOP VANDEVELD WAS A KIND AND COURTEOUS MAN WHO INSPIRED CHINIQUY TO GO SEE THAT BEAUTIFUL LAND, JUST WAITING FOR HIS FARMERS.

HE SAW THE BEAUTIFUL FIELDS . . . AND WROTE A LETTER TO BE PUBLISHED IN THE FRENCH CANADIAN NEWSPAPERS, TELLING OF WHAT HE FOUND.

HE NEVER DREAMED THE KIND OF REACTION IT WOULD CAUSE IN CANADA.

ALMOST ALL THE FARMERS IN QUEBEC PUT THEIR FARMS UP FOR SALE.

WE'VE **GOT** TO GO TO ILLINOIS!

THE PRICE OF LAND DROPPED BY HALF. IF THEY HAD LEFT, CANADA WOULD HAVE BEEN RUINED.

SOME PRAISED HIM FOR WRITING THAT LETTER, AND OTHERS CURSED HIM. HE WENT BACK TO CANADA.

THE BISHOP OF MONTREAL, CANADA, WANTED TO SEE CHINIQUY.

THE BISHOP WILL SEE YOU NOW.

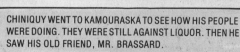

YOUR LETTER IS **TREASON!**

YOU ARE OUT TO **DESTROY** OUR WEALTHY PARISHES,

BY TAKING OUR PEOPLE TO THE UNITED STATES.

CHINIQUY TRIED TO EXPLAIN, BUT THE BISHOP OF MONTREAL SAW CHINIQUY AS A GREAT THREAT AND AN ENEMY.

HE GAVE CHINIQUY HIS BLESSING EVEN THOUGH HE WAS GOING TO GET RID OF CHINIQUY ONE WAY OR ANOTHER IN ORDER TO KEEP HIS POWER AND WEALTH.

CHINIQUY WENT TO KAMOURASKA TO SEE HOW HIS PEOPLE WERE DOING. THEY WERE STILL AGAINST LIQUOR. THEN HE SAW HIS OLD FRIEND, MR. BRASSARD.

CHINIQUY, THERE IS A PLOT TO DESTROY YOU BEFORE THE FARMERS FOLLOW YOU TO THE UNITED STATES.

THE BISHOP OF MONTREAL AND HIS PRIESTS ARE JEALOUS OF YOU.

BE ON GUARD!

A NOTE ARRIVED. THE BISHOP OF MONTREAL WANTED TO SEE CHINIQUY AGAIN, AND AS SOON AS POSSIBLE.

THIS TIME, THE BISHOP OF MONTREAL WAS VERY FRIENDLY . . . ALMOST TOO FRIENDLY.

AREN'T YOU THE CONFESSOR TO MRS. CHENIER?

YES, MY LORD.

AHHH . . . THAT IS GOOD, **VERY** GOOD.

YOU KNOW HER ONLY DAUGHTER IS A NUN?

OH, YES, MY LORD. I KNOW THAT.

COULD **YOU** TALK MRS. CHENIER INTO BECOMING A NUN ALSO?

WHY SHOULD SHE GIVE UP HER BEAUTIFUL COTTAGE FOR A GLOOMY NUNNERY?

BECAUSE HER BEAUTY AND WEALTH COULD CAUSE HER TO BE DECEIVED BY TEMPTATION.

I BELIEVE IT WOULD BE BETTER IF SHE FOUND HERSELF A GOOD HUSBAND INSTEAD.

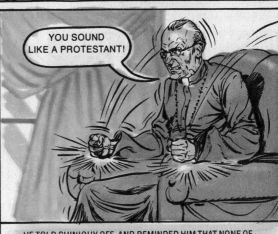

YOU SOUND LIKE A PROTESTANT!

HE TOLD CHINIQUY OFF, AND REMINDED HIM THAT NONE OF THE YOUNG LADIES WHO WENT TO HIM AS THEIR CONFESSOR EVER BECAME NUNS.

THIS WAS A BLACK MARK ON HIS RECORD.

FINALLY, THE BISHOP OF MONTREAL TOLD THE **REAL** REASON HE WANTED MRS. CHENIER A NUN.

MY FIRST REASON IS FOR THE SPIRITUAL GOOD

SHE WOULD RECEIVE FROM HER VOWS

OF PURITY AND POVERTY IN A NUNNERY.

MY SECOND IS . . .

SHE IS **RICH!** . . . AND WE NEED HER MONEY!

HER ONLY DAJGHTER IS ALREADY A NUN.

THIS WAY, WE GET **EVERYTHING!**

CHINIQUY TOLD HIM HOW NUNS CURSED THEIR MISERABLE LIVES IN A NUNNERY AND HE WOULD **NOT** DO THAT TO MRS. CHENIER. HE TURNED THE BISHOP DOWN FLAT!

THE BISHOP WAS BOILING MAD WHEN CHINIQUY LEFT HIS PALACE.

CHINIQUY TOLD HIS OLD FRIEND, MR. BRASSARD, WHAT HAD HAPPENED.

MR. BRASSARD, IF THE PEOPLE KNEW HOW MUCH MONEY HAS BEEN STOLEN

FROM THE INHERITANCE OF THOSE POOR NUNS BEFORE THEY WERE THROWN INTO THOSE DUNGEONS,* WE CALL NUNNERIES

THE PEOPLE WOULD HANG THEIR CONFESSORS.

I AGREE, BUT BE CAREFUL, MY FRIEND. THE BISHOP OF MONTREAL AND HIS MEN

WILL NEVER FORGIVE YOU FOR WHAT YOU DID.

MAY GOD PROTECT YOU.

"FIFTY YEARS IN THE 'CHURCH' OF ROME," P. 202

SEPT., 1851   A BEAUTIFUL GIRL CAME TO CHINIQUY'S CONFESSIONAL AND BRAGGED ABOUT HER ORGIES WITH PRIESTS. IT MADE HIM SICK.

I FORBID YOU TO COME BACK TO MY CONFESSIONAL AGAIN!

HE STOPPED HER COLD, AND ORDERED HER OUT OF THE CHURCH. HE KNEW HE WAS BEING SET UP.

A FEW WEEKS LATER, THE BISHOP DROPPED THE BOMB.

MR. BRASSARD, I CAN'T BELIEVE IT. MY POWERS AS A PRIEST ARE GONE. I'VE

BEEN BROKEN FOR A CRIME HE WON'T TALK ABOUT,

COMMITTED WITH SOMEONE HE WON'T NAME.

HE'LL **NEVER** TELL YOU WHO IT IS BECAUSE HE KNOWS YOU'RE INNOCENT.

CHINIQUY'S REPUTATION WAS BEING DESTROYED. HE FACED THE BISHOP OF MONTREAL.

I WILL **NOT** GIVE YOU THE NAME.

YOU ARE RUINED!

I HAVE NOTHING MORE TO DO WITH YOU.

THE BISHOP OF MONTREAL WAS A MONSTER BUT HE WAS CONSIDERED A SAINT BY HIS FLOCK.

GOD HELP ME.

CHINIQUY WAS GUILTY WITHOUT A TRIAL. HE DIDN'T KNOW THE CRIME OR WHO WAS INVOLVED.

HIS FAITH IN HIS CHURCH WAS BADLY SHAKEN. THESE "MEN OF GOD" WERE NOT AT ALL LIKE THE CHRIST THEY CLAIMED TO FOLLOW.

CHINIQUY WENT TO A JESUIT COLLEGE TO PRAY AND REST. HE TOLD THE DIRECTOR HIS PROBLEM.

WE'LL TAKE CARE OF IT, MR. CHINIQUY.

BEFORE YOUR VISIT IS AT AN END, THE BISHOP OF MONTREAL WILL BE

MOST HAPPY TO MAKE PEACE WITH YOU.

THE JESUITS BACKED CHINIQUY — FOUND THE GIRL, WHO HAPPENED TO BE A CLOSE FRIEND OF THE BISHOP, AND INVITED HER TO THE JESUIT COLLEGE. SHE WAS HONORED.

WHEN THE GIRL SAW CHINIQUY, SHE ALMOST FAINTED.

SHE BROKE DOWN, CONFESSED HER PART IN THE PLOT TO DESTROY CHINIQUY, FOUR COPIES WERE MADE OF HER CONFESSION BY THE DIRECTOR OF THE COLLEGE.
IT SAVED CHINIQUY'S REPUTATION.

THE BISHOP OF MONTREAL GAVE CHINIQUY BACK HIS POWER AS A PRIEST.

BEING A SHREWD POLITICIAN, BOURGET GAVE CHINIQUY GLOWING LETTERS OF RECOMMENDATION AND HIS PERSONAL BLESSING. THE BISHOP WAS ALSO AFRAID OF THE JESUITS.

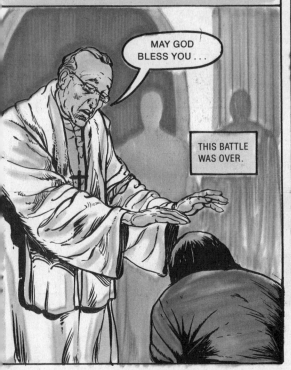

MAY GOD BLESS YOU . . .

THIS BATTLE WAS OVER.

CHINIQUY LEFT CANADA TO BEGIN A NEW CHAPTER IN HIS LIFE, IN THE UNITED STATES.

THE CANADIANS LOVED THIS MAN, AND IT WAS A GREAT LOSS TO THEM TO SEE HIM GO.

LITTLE DID HE DREAM GOD WOULD MOVE IN SUCH A STRANGE WAY AS TO HAVE HIM PLAY AN IMPORTANT ROLE IN THE LIFE OF A PRESIDENT.

THE GREAT WORK BEGAN IN EARNEST. CHINIQUY LEFT CHICAGO AND DROVE 3 DAYS THROUGH THE PRAIRIES TO A YOUNG COLONY CALLED BOURBONNAIS.

WELCOME, FATHER CHINIQUY . . . WELCOME!

HE WAS WARMLY GREETED BY REV. COURJEAULT, A FRENCH PRIEST WHO WAS THE PASTOR.

CHINIQUY TOLD THE PRIEST THAT BISHOP VANDEVELD OF CHICAGO WANTED HIM TO BUILD SETTLEMENTS FOR ROMAN CATHOLIC IMMIGRANTS LARGE ENOUGH TO RULE THE GOVERNMENT OF ILLINOIS.

INSTEAD OF JOY AND SUPPORT, HE SAW THE GREENEYED MONSTER OF JEALOUSY TAKE OVER REV. COURJEAULT. SITTING ACROSS FROM HIM WAS A NEW ENEMY. IT SHOOK UP CHINIQUY BECAUSE . . .

HE GOT THE SAME REACTION BACK IN CHICAGO FROM ANOTHER PRIEST NAMED REV. LEBEL.

I'M AS GOOD AS CHINIQUY. WHY DIDN'T THE BISHOP PICK ME?

SO NOW, CHINIQUY HAD TWO ENEMIES IN THE U.S. WHO WERE JEALOUS OF HIM. THEY BANDED TOGETHER TO STOP HIS WORK.

CHINIQUY PUSHED ON AND FOUND THE PLACE FOR HIS FARMERS. IT WAS CALLED ST. ANNE.

HE THANKED GOD FOR LETTING HIM FIND IT.

SOON TENTS APPEARED EVERYWHERE AS FAMILIES POURED IN. THEY PUT UP SMALL BUILDINGS SO THEY COULD MAKE IT THROUGH THE WINTERS. THE COLONY STARTED TO BLOSSOM.

EVERYONE IN ST. ANNE WORKED AND PRAYED TOGETHER. THE HEARTS OF THE PEOPLE WERE ONE WITH THEIR PRIEST. CHINIQUY GAVE ALL HIS MONEY AND ALL HE HAD TO BUILD THAT COMMUNITY FOR ROME. PEOPLE POURED IN FROM BELGIUM AND FRANCE. SOON NEW TOWNS STARTED TO SPRING UP.

LAKE MICHIGAN

CHICAGO

ILLINOIS

INDIANA

BOURBONNAIS

KANKAKEE

ST. ANNE

WHILE CHINIQUY WAS AT ST. ANNE, HIS ENEMIES WERE HARD AT WORK RUINING HIS FRIENDSHIP WITH BISHOP VANDEVELD.

THEY WERE SENDING LETTERS TO CANADA CONTAINING VICIOUS LIES ABOUT THE BISHOP.

THESE LETTERS WERE BEING PUBLISHED IN A WEEKLY NEWSPAPER.

SINCE THEY WERE SIGNED R.L.C., THE BISHOP THOUGHT CHINIQUY HAD WRITTEN THEM.

OH, MY GOD . . . WHY IS CHINIQUY DOING THIS TO ME?

BISHOP VANDEVELD BLESSED THE NEW CHAPEL AT ST. ANNE AND INVITED CHINIQUY TO GO WITH HIM TO BOURBONNAIS, WHICH HE DID.

WHY, CHINIQUY, WHY?

AFTER DINNER, THE BISHOP PULLED OUT THE NEWSPAPERS AND ASKED CHINIQUY WHY HE HAD WRITTEN THOSE TERRIBLE LETTERS.

CHINIQUY DENIED WRITING THEM, AND IT WAS DISCOVERED THAT THE PRIEST, COURJEAULT, WAS THE AUTHOR. HE CONFESSED AND BEGGED FOR MERCY.

HE SHED TEARS, PROMISING TO BE A BETTER PRIEST.

IN THE NAME OF OUR CRUCIFIED SAVIOR,

I ASK YOU TO FORGIVE ME.

BOTH THE BISHOP AND CHINIQUY FORGAVE HIM. ALL THREE WERE EMOTIONALLY DRAINED BY THIS AWFUL EXPERIENCE.

CHINIQUY WENT FOR HIS AFTERNOON PRAYERS AND LATER, HE SAW COURJEAULT STAGGERING. CHINIQUY ASKED HIM WHAT WAS WRONG.

DEAR CHINIQUY, I HAVE TO TELL YOU OF ANOTHER DARK MYSTERY IN MY MISERABLE LIFE.

FOR OVER A YEAR, I HAVE LIVED WITH THE BEADLE'S* DAUGHTER AS MY WIFE.

AND NOW SHE IS PREGNANT!

*A MINOR OFFICIAL IN A PARISH, LIKE AN USHER.

SHE WANTS $500.00, OR SHE WILL EXPOSE ME PUBLICLY TO THE BISHOP AND THE PEOPLE.

WHAT SHOULD I DO?

THE PEOPLE THOUGHT THEIR PRIEST WAS SUCH A HOLY MAN . . . AND NOW REV. COURJEAULT WAS IN A BIG FAT MESS.

HE CONFESSED TO THE BISHOP, WHO ALMOST FAINTED. THE BISHOP DECIDED TO SEND THE GIRL TO THE HOME IN CANADA THAT THE CHURCH PROVIDED FOR GIRLS WHO BECAME PREGNANT BY PRIESTS.

REV. COURJEAULT TELLS ME THAT NO ONE KNOWS ABOUT THIS.

HE WANTS TO STAY HERE, AND HAS PROMISED NOT TO CREATE ANY MORE SCANDALS.

I SWEAR . . . I WILL BE A GOOD PRIEST FROM NOW ON.

MONEY WAS RAISED. THE GIRL LEFT FOR CANADA. THE PEOPLE WEREN'T BLIND. THEY FIGURED OUT WHAT HAD HAPPENED.

FIVE DAYS LATER, A GROUP FROM BOURBONNAIS VISITED CHINIQUY AND BEGGED HIM TO COME TELL THEIR PRIEST TO LEAVE THEIR COMMUNITY.

CHINIQUY NEVER DREAMED IT WOULD BE AN ACT OF WAR.

CHINIQUY WENT TO BOURBONNAIS AND IN THE PRESENCE OF 4 WITNESSES, TOLD COURJEAULT THAT EVERYONE KNEW ABOUT HIS AFFAIR WITH THE BEADLE'S DAUGHTER. COURJEAULT WAS SHATTERED, AND LEFT FOR CHICAGO. BUT TO EVERYONE'S SURPRISE, A FEW DAYS LATER, HE ARROGANTLY RETURNED.

HE BROKE UP THE CHURCH SERVICE AND ACCUSED CHINIQUY.

YOU STOLE MY CHURCH FROM ME

AND I'M HERE TO TAKE IT BACK!

DISGUSTED WITH COURJEAULT, CHINIQUY WENT BACK TO ST. ANNE. THE PEOPLE OF BOURBONNAIS REFUSED TO ATTEND THEIR CHURCH WHILE THE PRIEST WAS THERE. REV. COURJEAULT TOOK OFF FOR FRANCE IN TOTAL DISGRACE.

HE ONLY STAYED IN FRANCE FOR ONE MONTH, AND THEN HE WAS SPOTTED IN INDIANA NEAR THE BORDER OF ILLINOIS.

I'LL GET EVEN!

HE WAS LIKE A MADMAN, THREATENING TO BURN DOWN THE CHURCH IN BOURBONNAIS.

CHINIQUY TRIED TO GET THE CHURCH INSURED, BUT IT WASN'T TOTALLY BUILT. SO THEY WORKED HARD TO FINISH THE CHURCH, AND IT WAS BEAUTIFUL.

THEY HAD ONE GREAT SERVICE AND THAT EVENING, JUST ONE DAY BEFORE THEY COULD BUY THE INSURANCE . . . .

THE TWO PRIESTS, LEBEL AND COURJEAULT, AND THEIR ARSONISTS, REDUCED IT TO ASHES.

AFTER THE FIRE, REV. COURJEAULT PUT HIMSELF INTO A MONASTERY TO ESCAPE.

IT WAS TOO MUCH FOR THE DEAR OLD BISHOP OF CHICAGO. HE WANTED TO GIVE UP. HE BROKE DOWN AND TOLD CHINIQUY THE WHOLE ROTTEN STORY.

I'M GOING TO TELL YOU SOMETHING SO CONFIDENTIAL THAT NO ONE ELSE KNOWS ABOUT IT.

THE PRIESTS OF MY DIOCESE ARE SO EVIL THAT IF I FOLLOWED REGULATIONS,

I WOULD BE FORCED TO INTERDICT* ALL BUT THREE.

*STRIP THEM OF THEIR POWERS.

THEY ARE ALL EITHER NOTORIOUS DRUNKARDS, OR HAVE MISTRESSES. SEVERAL HAVE HAD CHILDREN BY THEIR OWN NIECES, AND TWO BY THEIR OWN SISTERS.

I DON'T BELIEVE 10 OF THEM BELIEVE IN GOD.

RELIGION TO THEM IS NOTHING BUT A WELL-PAYING COMEDY.

IF I RAISE A FINGER AGAINST THEM, THEN THEY WILL DO TO ME WHAT THEY DID TO THE BISHOP BEFORE ME.

HE WAS POISONED!

I'VE ASKED THE POPE FOR A TRANSFER. THE RESPONSIBILITY HERE IS KILLING ME.

THEY WEPT TOGETHER OVER THE SCANDALS. CHINIQUY LOVED THIS MAN LIKE HIS OWN FATHER AND LOOKED UPON HIM AS A GREAT MAN OF GOD.

CHINIQUY HAD COMPLETE CONFIDENCE IN HIM AND FELT HE WAS TRULY WORTHY TO BE A BISHOP OF CHRIST.

THAT DEAR BISHOP IS SO FAITHFUL!

CHINIQUY LOOKED UP TO BISHOP VANDEVELD. HE ADMIRED HIS INTELLIGENCE, HIS KIND HEART AND THE SINCERITY OF THIS FAITH.

CHINIQUY WENT TO SLEEP. THE BISHOP SPENT THE NIGHT IN HIS HOME.

THE NEXT MORNING, CHINIQUY WENT TO GET THE BISHOP UP FOR BREAKFAST.

HE MADE A HORRIBLE DISCOVERY.

BURP

THE BISHOP WAS A DRUNKARD.

"KNOW YE NOT THAT THE UNRIGHTEOUS SHALL NOT INHERIT THE KINGDOM OF GOD? BE NOT DECEIVED: NEITHER FORNICATORS, NOR IDOLATERS, NOR ADULTERERS, NOR EFFIMINATE, NOR ABUSERS OF THEMSELVES WITH MANKIND, NOR THIEVES, NOR COVETOUS, NOR DRUNKARDS, NOR REVILERS, NOR EXTORTIONERS, SHALL INHERIT THE KINGDOM OF GOD."

(I COR. 6:9-10)

IT WAS LIKE GOD'S VOICE CRYING TO CHINIQUY THROUGH HIS SLEEPLESS NIGHTS, SAYING . . .

"WHAT ARE YOU DOING HERE, HELPING TO BUILD THE POWER OF A CHURCH WHICH IS A DEN OF THIEVES, DRUNKARDS AND IMPURE ATHEISTS?

"A CHURCH GOVERNED BY MEN WHOM YOU KNOW TO BE GODLESS, SWINDLERS AND VILE COMEDIANS?

"DON'T YOU SEE? YOU DON'T FOLLOW THE WORD OF GOD, BUT THE LYING TRADITIONS OF MEN WHEN YOU AGREE TO BOW YOUR KNEES BEFORE SUCH MEN?

"COME OUT* OF THAT CHURCH! BREAK THE CHAINS BY WHICH YOU ARE TIED LIKE A MISERABLE SLAVE TO THE FEET OF SUCH MEN."
*II COR. 6:14-18

"TAKE UP THE GOSPEL FOR YOUR ONLY GUIDE, AND CHRIST FOR YOUR ONLY RULER!"

CHINIQUY WAS MISERABLE.

BISHOP VANDEVELD RECEIVED HIS TRANSFER. HE BECAME THE BISHOP OF NATCHEZ, LOUISIANA.

THE NEW BISHOP OF CHICAGO WAS AN IRISHMAN NAMED O'REGAN.

O'REGAN'S FIRST OFFICIAL ACT WAS TO SUE BISHOP VANDEVELD. HE CALLED HIM A THIEF AND CLAIMED HE TOOK $100,000 FROM THE CHICAGO DIOCESE TO NATCHEZ.

EXTRA
VANDEVELD IS LIAR
CLAIMS BISHOP O'REGAN
THIEF

BOTH BISHOPS HIRED THE BEST LAWYERS. IT WAS A HORRIBLE SCANDAL. IT APPEARED IN NEWSPAPERS NATION-WIDE. THE POPE HAD TO BREAK IT UP. EACH MAN ENDED UP WITH $50,000.

ANOTHER ACTION WAS QUIETLY GOING ON ACROSS THE SEAS. THE JESUITS IN THE VATICAN WERE BUSY PLANNING THE DESTRUCTION OF THE U.S. BY SENDING AGENTS INTO THE NORTH AND SOUTH TO FAN THE RED-HOT ISSUE OF SLAVERY.

IF THINGS WOULD GO THE WAY THEY PLANNED, THE UNITED STATES WOULD SOON EXPLODE INTO CIVIL WAR, AND DESTROY THE COUNTRY.

CHINIQUY MET BISHOP O'REGAN FOR THE FIRST TIME IN DECEMBER OF 1854 . . . A DAY HE WOULD NEVER FORGET.

IS THIS THE DEED TO THE ELEVEN ACRES OF LAND THAT YOU BOUGHT ON WHICH THE CHAPEL OF ST. ANNE WAS BUILT?

YES, MY LORD.

WELL, IT'S NO GOOD! YOUR NAME SHOULD **NEVER** BE ON IT.

BUT I BOUGHT THAT LAND MYSELF!

O'REGAN WANTED TO TAKE THE 11 ACRES AND THE CHAPEL FOR HIMSELF.

BUT BISHOP VANDEVELD ACCEPTED IT AS VALID!

I DON'T CARE **WHAT** HE DID . . .

YOU GET ME ANOTHER TITLE.

HE THREW THE DEED ON THE FLOOR. CHINIQUY PICKED IT UP AND WENT BACK TO ST. ANNE.

IN HIS HEART, CHINIQUY KNEW A VIOLENT STORM WAS COMING.

CHINIQUY WROTE BISHOP O'REGAN, ASKING TO BE RELEASED FROM HIS DUTIES AT BOURBONNAIS SO HE COULD GO BACK TO WORK AT ST. ANNE. HE GOT HIS WISH.

GOOD-BYE, MY FRIENDS. BISHOP O'REGAN SAYS HE'LL SEND A FINE MAN TO REPLACE ME.

COME BACK AND VISIT US OFTEN, FATHER CHINIQUY.

THE PRIEST WHO REPLACED HIM IMMEDIATELY GOT INTO TROUBLE AND WAS THROWN OUT. AND SO, O'REGAN SENT ANOTHER ONE.

HIS NAME WAS FATHER LEBEL. O'REGAN GOT HIM OUT OF CHICAGO BECAUSE OF ANOTHER NASTY SCANDAL, AND GAVE HIM BOURBONNAIS.

LEBEL WOULD PLAY A VERY BIG PART IN CHINIQUY'S LIFE. HE WAS ONE OF HIS DEADLIEST ENEMIES.

ANOTHER PRIEST WHO WAS KICKED OUT OF BELGIUM AND THE PRIESTHOOD, CAME TO CHICAGO AND BECAME RICH. HE OWNED A HOUSE OF PROSTITUTION.

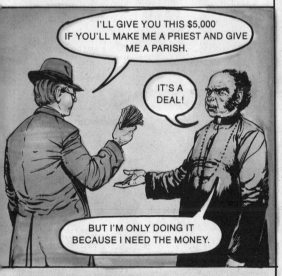

I'LL GIVE YOU THIS $5,000 IF YOU'LL MAKE ME A PRIEST AND GIVE ME A PARISH.

IT'S A DEAL!

BUT I'M ONLY DOING IT BECAUSE I NEED THE MONEY.

O'REGAN TOOK HIS MONEY AND MADE HIM THE SPIRITUAL LEADER OF KANKAKEE, ILLINOIS. THIS WAS CHINIQUY'S NEW NEIGHBOR.

DR. RIVERA, (EX-JESUIT) SAYS THAT, "EVEN TODAY, FOR A LARGE SUM, A MAN MAY BUY THE POSITION OF A CARDINAL IN THE INSTITUTION, AND BE GIVEN ALL THE POWER THAT GOES WITH THAT TITLE."

THE TWO PRIESTS VISITED CHINIQUY WHEN THEY WERE DRUNK. CHINIQUY KICKED THEM OUT AND TOLD THEM NEVER TO COME BACK AGAIN.

O'REGAN FOUND OUT AND BLASTED CHINIQUY IN A LETTER FOR NOT BEING FRIENDLY.

I WOULD GIVE *ANYTHING* TO THE ONE WHO WOULD HELP ME GET RID OF THAT UNMANAGABLE CHINIQUY!

IF YOU PAY THE EXPENSES OF A LAW SUIT, I'LL GET CHINIQUY PUT IN JAIL.

VERY GOOD, MR. SPINK. I'LL BACK YOU.

SPINK WAS A LAND SHARK WHO HAD TRIED TO CHEAT THE FRENCH CANADIAN IMMIGRANTS, BUT CHINIQUY SPOILED HIS PLANS. HIS HATRED FOR CHINIQUY WAS AS DEEP AS O'REGAN'S.

SPINK TOOK CHINIQUY TO COURT IN KANKAKEE, AND LOST THE CASE.

RIGHT AFTER THAT, BISHOP O'REGAN CAME TO ST. ANNE ON A SURPRISE VISIT. HE BROUGHT CHINIQUY'S TWO MISERABLE NEIGHBORS WITH HIM.

WE'VE COME TO ADMINISTER THE SACRAMENT OF CONFIRMATION.

CHINIQUY GOT THE BISHOP ASIDE AND PROTESTED ABOUT THOSE 2 PRIESTS COMING BACK TO ST. ANNE. EVERYBODY KNEW ABOUT THEIR TERRIBLE HISTORIES. CHINIQUY WAS AFRAID THEY MIGHT DESTROY THE FAITH OF HIS PEOPLE.

CHINIQUY USED THE GOSPEL TO MAKE HIS POINT. IT CLEARLY TELLS US NOT TO ASSOCIATE WITH SUCH EVIL MEN.

Psalm 1:1

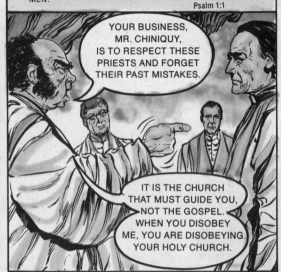

YOUR BUSINESS, MR. CHINIQUY, IS TO RESPECT THESE PRIESTS AND FORGET THEIR PAST MISTAKES.

IT IS THE CHURCH THAT MUST GUIDE YOU, NOT THE GOSPEL. WHEN YOU DISOBEY ME, YOU ARE DISOBEYING YOUR HOLY CHURCH.

AFTER DINNER, CHINIQUY AND BISHOP O'REGAN WENT FOR A WALK. O'REGAN WANTED TO SEE HIS LITTLE HOUSE AND GARDEN.

WHERE DID YOU GET THE MONEY TO BUY THIS LAND AND BUILD THIS HOUSE?

I EARNED IT BY HARD WORK AND THE SWEAT OF MY BROW.

I WANT THAT HOUSE AND THAT PIECE OF LAND.

SO DO I!

YOU **MUST** GIVE ME THAT HOUSE AND THE LAND ON WHICH IT STANDS.

CHINIQUY REFUSED. HE COULDN'T GIVE IT AWAY AS LONG AS HE NEEDED IT FOR HIS WORK.

YOU'RE A BAD PRIEST. YOU HAVE NO RIGHT TO OWN **ANY** PROPERTY.

IF YOU CAN SHOW ME ANY LAW THAT FORBIDS ME TO OWN IT . . . THEN I'LL TURN THE PROPERTY OVER TO YOU.

I'LL GET THE LAW PASSED, MYSELF!

YOU ARE AN INSOLENT PRIEST!

AND I'LL MAKE YOU PAY FOR IT!

O'REGAN TOOK OFF FOR CHICAGO. CHINIQUY COULDN'T BELIEVE IT. THE BISHOP HAD JUST TRIED TO STEAL HIS HOME AWAY FROM HIM.

CHINIQUY HAD GIVEN BIBLES TO HIS PEOPLE, WHICH OUTRAGED BISHOP O'REGAN. THINGS WENT FROM BAD TO WORSE.

NEWSPAPERS WERE BEGINNING TO TELL OF THE THINGS BISHOP O'REGAN WAS DOING. CHINIQUY WENT TO CHICAGO TO FIND OUT FOR HIMSELF IF THESE THINGS WERE TRUE.

HIS FIRST STOP WAS TO SEE THE FRENCH CANADIANS IN CHICAGO.

IT'S TRUE, FATHER CHINIQUY. THE BISHOP TOOK ALL OF THE BEAUTIFUL VESTMENTS* THAT WE BOUGHT FOR OUR CHURCH,

AND HE PUT THEM IN HIS OWN CHURCH FOR HIMSELF.

*THE EXPENSIVE CEREMONIAL ROBES THE PRIESTS WORE ON SPECIAL OCCASIONS.

THEN HE SAW THE GERMAN CATHOLICS IN CHICAGO.

BISHOP O'REGAN SWINDLED US OUT OF A FINE LOT THAT WAS GIVEN TO US TO BUILD OUR CHURCH ON.

HE SOLD IT FOR $40,000.

HE POCKETED THE MONEY FOR HIS OWN PRIVATE USE WITHOUT TELLING US ABOUT IT.

THAT'S TRUE.

THERE WERE ALSO REPORTS THAT O'REGAN WAS EVEN SELLING THE BONES OF THE DEAD!

CHINIQUY WENT TO THE CEMETERY TO SEE IF THIS WAS TRUE. HE SAW CARTS OF SAND COMING FROM THE ROMAN CATHOLIC GRAVEYARD.

MAY I EXAMINE THE SAND IN YOUR CARTS?

OF COURSE, FATHER.

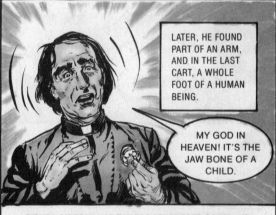

LATER, HE FOUND PART OF AN ARM, AND IN THE LAST CART, A WHOLE FOOT OF A HUMAN BEING.

MY GOD IN HEAVEN! IT'S THE JAW BONE OF A CHILD.

BISHOP O'REGAN HAD THE OLD FENCE TORN DOWN AND BUILT A NEW ONE SEVERAL FEET INSIDE THE OLD LOCATION. O'REGAN CLAIMED HE WAS ONLY SELLING SAND.

TO QUIET THE PEOPLE, CHINIQUY PAID A VISIT TO O'REGAN. HE TOLD HIM WHAT A TERRIBLE IMPACT ALL THIS WAS HAVING ON THE ROMAN CATHOLICS. O'REGAN BLEW HIS STACK.

WHAT SPINK TOLD ME ABOUT YOU IS TRUE! YOU **ARE** THE HEAD OF MY ENEMIES.

LISTEN TO ME, CHINIQUY!

FOR YOUR INFORMATION, THERE IS NOW A LAW IN THE U.S. THAT MAKES EVERY ONE OF US BISHOPS A CORPORATION . . .

THE LAW GIVES ME THE RIGHT TO TAKE **ALL** OF THE ROMAN CATHOLIC CHURCH PROPERTIES FOR MYSELF!

ALL THOSE THINGS ARE MINE! I CAN DO WHATEVER I WANT WITH THEM, AND YOU **WILL** BE SILENT WHEN I TAKE THEM AWAY FROM YOU!

YOU REBEL AGAINST GOD HIMSELF WHEN YOU TRY TO STOP ME FROM TAKING YOUR PROPERTY.

FURTHERMORE, I WON'T PAY YOU A PENNY FOR IT. EVERYTHING BELONGS TO **ME**!

HE WARNED CHINIQUY THAT IF HE DIDN'T MAKE THE ROMAN CATHOLICS SHUT UP AND START RESPECTING THEIR HONORABLE BISHOP OF CHICAGO, CHINIQUY WOULD SOON HEAR FROM HIM AGAIN. IT WAS A THREAT!

THE CIVIL WAR WAS GETTING CLOSER.

A LITTLE BOOK HAD BEEN PUBLISHED, CALLED "UNCLE TOM'S CABIN."

THIS IS HORRIBLE. WE'VE **GOT** TO STOP SLAVERY!

THIS BOOK WAS SELLING ALL OVER THE NORTHERN STATES. IT WAS PACKED WITH DRAMA AND EMOTION. THE PEOPLE WHO READ IT WERE OUTRAGED.

BACK IN CHICAGO, BISHOP O'REGAN WAS TRYING HIS BEST TO GET RID OF CHINIQUY. HE WANTED TO INTERDICT HIM BUT HE HAD NO GROUNDS.

I'VE GOT A NEW IDEA TO GET RID OF CHINIQUY.

WHAT ARE YOUR PLANS, MR. SPINK?

SPINK (THE LAND SHARK) HAD COOKED UP MORE PHONEY CHARGES AGAINST CHINIQUY. IF CHINIQUY WAS FOUND GUILTY, HIS CAREER WOULD BE RUINED, AND O'REGAN COULD INTERDICT HIM. GOD WAS WITH CHINIQUY. THE JURY FOUND HIM INNOCENT ON NOV. 13, 1855.

THE VICTORY DIDN'T LAST LONG. CHINIQUY'S LAWYERS TOLD HIM THAT MR. SPINK APPEALED FOR A RE-TRIAL IN THE CITY OF URBANA, ILLINOIS, IN CHAMPAIGN COUNTY.

CHINIQUY COULD NOT AFFORD TO BRING HIS 20 WITNESSES THAT GREAT DISTANCE. THIS TIME, HE WAS ALONE IN THIS FIGHT.

SPINK SAW TO IT THAT CHINIQUY WOULD REMAIN A PRISONER UNDER BAIL IN THE HANDS OF THE SHERIFF UNTIL THE 19TH OF MAY, 1856 (6 MONTHS).

CHINIQUY FELT THIS TIME HIS ENEMIES WOULD WIN. BUT GOD HAD OTHER PLANS.

A STRANGER WHO WANTED TO KEEP HIS IDENTITY SECRET CAME TO CHINIQUY WITH VALUABLE INFORMATION.

I HAVE FOLLOWED THIS TRIAL FROM THE BEGINNING. YOUR PROSECUTOR, SPINK, IS ONLY A TOOL* FOR BISHOP O'REGAN.

BECAUSE YOU ARE A PRIEST, YOU ARE NOT ONLY FIGHTING BISHOP O'REGAN, YOU ARE FIGHTING ALL THE BISHOPS WORLD WIDE. EVEN THOUGH THEY HATE WHAT O'REGAN IS DOING, THEY WILL UNITE BEHIND HIM, USING ALL THE WEALTH AND INFLUENCE AT THEIR DISPOSAL, TO SILENCE YOU.

THERE IS A GOOD CHANCE THE JURY IN URBANA WILL BELIEVE THOSE LIES.

THERE IS ONLY ONE LAWYER WHO CAN SAVE YOU, AND HIS NAME IS ABRAHAM LINCOLN.

I'VE NEVER HEARD OF ABRAHAM LINCOLN.

HE IS THE BEST LAWYER AND THE MOST HONEST MAN IN ILLINOIS.

CHINIQUY WIRED LINCOLN FOR HELP. THIS WAS HIS REPLY: "YES, I WILL DEFEND YOUR HONOR AND YOUR LIFE AT THE NEXT MAY TERM IN URBANA."

*DR. RIVERA, (EX-JESUIT), STATES: "UNKNOWN TO CHINIQUY, HE WAS AT WAR WITH THE ENTIRE ROMAN CATHOLIC INSTITUTION, BECAUSE IN THEIR EYES, HE WAS A REBELLIOUS PRIEST, FIGHTING HIS BISHOP. IT COULD NOT BE TOLERATED. SPINK WAS ONLY A FRONT MAN, OR DECOY. ROME HAS ALWAYS USED THIS TECHNIQUE SO THEY COULDN'T BE BLAMED FOR ANY OF THE CRIMES AGAINST NATIONS OR INDIVIDUALS."

ON THE 19TH OF MAY, 1856, CHINIQUY MET ABRAHAM LINCOLN.

CHINIQUY SAID IT WAS IMPOSSIBLE TO TALK WITH HIM FOR 5 MINUTES WITHOUT LOVING HIM. THERE WAS SUCH AN EXPRESSION OF KINDNESS AND HONESTY IN HIS FACE.

MR. CHINIQUY, YOU WERE MISTAKEN WHEN YOU SENT ME A TELEGRAM AND SAID THAT YOU WERE UNKNOWN TO ME.

I KNOW YOU BY REPUTATION AS A STRICT OPPONENT OF THE TYRANNY* OF YOUR BISHOP.

THEY BECAME GOOD FRIENDS.

*TYRANNY: AN ACT OF BRUTAL RULE WITH ABSOLUTE AUTHORITY.

THE TWO LYING PRIESTS TESTIFIED AGAINST CHINIQUY, AND LINCOLN DEMOLISHED THEIR TESTIMONY, AS WELL AS THE OTHER PHONEY WITNESSES WHO ATTACKED HIM.

REV. LEBEL   REV. CARTHUVAL

ON THE 11TH OF JULY, CHINIQUY WOULD HAVE BEEN FOUND INNOCENT, BUT ONE IRISH ROMAN CATHOLIC IN THE JURY HELD OUT AND CLAIMED HE WAS GUILTY AND WOULD NOT CHANGE HIS MIND. IT WAS A HUNG JURY.

SO THERE HAD TO BE A NEW TRIAL. IT WAS POSTPONED UNTIL THE FALL, THE 20TH OF OCTOBER, 1856.

CHINIQUY GOT DEEPER INTO HIS BIBLE FOR STRENGTH. HE READ IN ISAIAH . . . "FEAR THOU NOT: FOR I AM WITH THEE."   (ISA. 41:10)

BISHOP O'REGAN CONTINUED TO PERSECUTE THE FRENCH CANADIANS IN CHICAGO.

O'REGAN THEN SOLD THEIR BEAUTIFUL LITTLE CHURCH AND MOVED IT INTO AN IRISH CATHOLIC NEIGHBORHOOD.

CHINIQUY WAS ORDERED TO REPORT TO O'REGAN.

BECAUSE YOU ARE SUCH A TROUBLE-MAKER, I'M SENDING YOU TO KAHOKIA, ILLINOIS.

IF YOU ARE NOT THERE BY THE 15TH OF SEPTEMBER, I'LL INTERDICT YOU, AND HAVE YOU EXCOMMUNICATED.

THIS WOULD MAKE CHINIQUY LOOK MORE GUILTY WHEN THE NEXT TRIAL CAME UP.

HIS APPEALS TO O'REGAN FELL ON DEAF EARS.

I WILL DO ALL THAT RELIGION AND HONOR WILL ALLOW ME, TO PROTECT MY NAME.

HE WARNED O'REGAN THAT HE WOULD NOT GO DOWN WITHOUT A FIGHT.

WHEN CHINIQUY GOT BACK TO ST. ANNE, THE DRUNKEN PRIESTS (HIS NEIGHBORS) WERE TELLING EVERYONE THAT O'REGAN HAD ALREADY INTERDICTED CHINIQUY, AND THEY WERE COMING TO TAKE OVER THE COLONY.

CHINIQUY GOT HIS FLOCK TOGETHER.

WHAT OUR BISHOP DID TO THE FRENCH CANADIANS OF CHICAGO, HE NOW WANTS TO DO TO US.

WITH GOD'S HELP WE WILL DEFEND OUR RIGHTS AS CHRISTIANS AND AS AMERICAN CITIZENS.

CHINIQUY HAD FOUND OUT SEPT. 3, 1856 WAS THE DATE SET FOR HIS EXCOMMUNICATION. HE TOLD HIS CONGREGATION WHAT WAS COMING, AND TO BE POLITE.

AT AROUND 2 P.M., SEPT. 3RD, 3,000 PEOPLE GATHERED ON THE HILL AT ST. ANNE. WHEN THE 3 DRUNKEN PRIESTS STEPPED OUT OF THEIR CARRIAGE, THE CROWD BEGAN TO CHEER. SHAKING FROM HEAD TO FOOT, ONE OF THE PRIESTS READ THE DOCUMENT AND NAILED IT TO THE CHURCH DOOR. THE PRIESTS LOST NO TIME IN GETTING OUT OF THERE.

CHINIQUY WAS EXCOMMUNICATED. SO WAS ANYONE ELSE WHO STOOD WITH HIM. BUT . . . BISHOP O'REGAN'S SIGNATURE WAS NOT ON THE PAPER.

THE PEOPLE OF ST. ANNE WERE 100% BEHIND CHINIQUY. THEY WROTE A POWERFUL LETTER EXPOSING THE CRIMES OF O'REGAN. THEY SAID IF HE'D TREAT THEM AS A FATHER INSTEAD OF A MASTER, THEY WOULD RESPECT HIM. IT WAS SIGNED BY 500 PEOPLE, AND PUBLISHED IN ALMOST EVERY PAPER IN THE U.S.

I'LL FIX THEM FOR THIS!

BISHOP O'REGAN WROTE AN ARTICLE DEFENDING HIS REASON FOR DESTROYING THE FRENCH CANADIAN CHURCH . . . IT WAS FILLED WITH LIES.

CHINIQUY THEN PUBLISHED THE MOST DEVASTATING LETTER EVER WRITTEN BY A PRIEST. IT HIT LIKE A BOMB. PRIESTS ALL OVER AMERICA TOLD CHINIQUY THEY WERE WITH HIM.

GOOD FOR CHINIQUY.

HAW HAW . . . GREAT!

BUT THEY WERE ALL AFRAID TO PUBLICLY BACK HIM.

O'REGAN GOT HOLD OF SPINK AND LEBEL, AND COOKED UP A FOOL-PROOF PLOT AGAINST CHINIQUY THAT EVEN ABRAHAM LINCOLN COULDN'T HELP.

HAW, HAW . . . TO THE END OF CHINIQUY!

I'LL DRINK TO THAT!

THEY BELIEVED AT LONG LAST THAT CHINIQUY WOULD GO TO JAIL, AND O'REGAN WOULD SEE THE LAST OF HIS ENEMY.

THE FIRST WITNESS CALLED WAS THE PRIEST, LEBEL.

CHINIQUY IS ONE OF THE VILEST (DIRTY, OR FOUL) MEN AROUND . . .

EVERYWHERE I GO, THERE ARE STORIES ABOUT THE TERRIBLE THINGS HE HAS DONE.

HE TOLD QUITE A FEW STORIES WHICH WERE COMPLETE LIES TO DESTROY CHINIQUY. BUT, OF COURSE, HE SAID HE DIDN'T KNOW IF THEY WERE TRUE OR NOT BECAUSE HE NEVER INVESTIGATED THEM.

NOW THE STAGE WAS SET. LEBEL WAS GOING TO DESTROY CHINIQUY WITH HIS NEWEST CHARGE. THE JURY WAS ALL EARS.

I HATE TO REVEAL THIS TO THE WORLD ABOUT MR. CHINIQUY,

BUT SINCE IT INVOLVES MY SISTER, MADAM BOSSEY...

...IF I AM TO SPEAK THE TRUTH BEFORE GOD...

THEN THE SAD TRUTH **MUST** BE TOLD.

IN A CHOKING VOICE HE IMPLIED CHINIQUY HAD TRIED TO RAPE HIS SISTER.

SHE, HERSELF, HAS TOLD ME THE WHOLE STORY WHILE UNDER OATH.

SHE WOULD BE HERE TO UNMASK THAT WICKED MAN TODAY BEFORE THE WHOLE WORLD... IF (SOB)... IF SHE WERE NOT SO SICK AT HOME!

POOR CHINIQUY WAS HIT WITH A THUNDERBOLT — RIGHT FROM THE PIT OF HELL. LEBEL PUT ON A BEAUTIFUL PERFORMANCE.

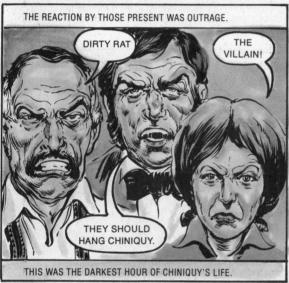

THE REACTION BY THOSE PRESENT WAS OUTRAGE.

DIRTY RAT

THE VILLAIN!

THEY SHOULD HANG CHINIQUY.

THIS WAS THE DARKEST HOUR OF CHINIQUY'S LIFE.

THEN ABRAHAM LINCOLN BROKE THE SILENCE.

HE SLASHED AT LEBEL'S TESTIMONY TO DISCREDIT HIM.

12 WITNESSES WERE BROUGHT IN FROM BOURBONNAIS WHO WERE IN REV. LEBEL'S PARISH WHEN HE WAS THEIR PRIEST.
THEY SAID HE WAS A DRUNKEN LIAR, AND THEY WOULDN'T BELIEVE A WORD HE SAID.

BUT LEBEL'S ATTACK HAD BEEN SUCCESSFUL.

I WILL TRY TOMORROW TO DESTROY HIS TESTIMONY, BUT I SEE GREAT DANGERS AHEAD.

I BELIEVE EVERYTHING HE SAID WAS A LIE, BUT MY FEAR IS THAT THE JURY BELIEVES HIM.

THE ONLY WAY TO DESTROY THE POWER OF A FALSE WITNESS IS BY ANOTHER DIRECT TESTIMONY AGAINST WHAT HE HAS SAID...

OR BY SHOWING FROM HIS LIPS THAT HE PERJURED* HIMSELF.

LEBEL DIDN'T TELL US WHEN THIS EVENT TOOK PLACE, SO WE CAN'T EVEN ESTABLISH AN ALIBI.

I KNOW YOU ARE INNO-CENT, BUT I'M AFRAID THIS COULD END WITH A PRISON TERM FOR YOU.

I'M SURE MADAM BOSSEY IS FAKING HER ILLNESS.

BUT IF SOME JUSTICE OF THE PEACE GETS HER TEST-IMONY, IT WILL BE HARD TO FIGHT,

BECAUSE EVERYONE IS FEELING SORRY FOR HER.

*TO LIE WHEN HE SWORE TO TELL THE TRUTH.

THE ONLY WAY TO BE SURE OF YOUR RECEIVING A FAVORABLE VERDICT TOMORROW IS IF GOD ALMIGHTY TAKES OUR PART IN PROVING YOUR INNOCENCE.

GO AND PRAY TO HIM!

CHINIQUY'S OWN CHURCH WAS DESTROYING HIM WITH THE WORST KIND OF LIES — HIS HONOR AND GOOD NAME WOULD BE RUINED FOREVER.

TOMORROW HE WOULD BE SENTENCED AND FOUND GUILTY OF A CRIME HE DIDN'T COMMIT.

OH, MY GOD, HAVE MERCY ON ME. COME TO MY HELP AND SAVE ME.

CHINIQUY WEPT BEFORE THE LORD INTO THE DARK HOURS OF THE NIGHT. HE FELT GOD HAD FORSAKEN HIM.

3 A.M.

KNOCK
KNOCK
KNOCK

WHO'S THERE?

THERE STOOD ABRAHAM LINCOLN, WITH HIS FACE BEAMING WITH JOY. (CHINIQUY SAID LINCOLN WAS ONE OF THE NOBLEST MEN HEAVEN HAD EVER GIVEN TO EARTH.)

CHEER UP MR. CHINIQUY . . .

I HAVE THOSE PERJURED PRIESTS IN MY HANDS.

THEIR DEVILISH PLOT HAS BEEN EXPOSED. IF THEY DON'T LEAVE TOWN BEFORE THE SUN COMES UP,

THEY WILL SURELY BE LYNCHED!*

BLESS THE LORD . . . YOU ARE SAVED!

GOD HAD MOVED AGAIN, AND ANSWERED CHINIQUY'S PRAYERS IN A MOST AMAZING WAY.

*LYNCHED: AN ANGRY MOB GRABS SOMEONE AND HANGS HIM WITHOUT A TRIAL.

WHEN LEBEL HAD GIVEN HIS LYING TESTIMONY AGAINST CHINIQUY, A NEWSPAPER REPORTER TELEGRAPHED THE STORY TO THE CHICAGO NEWSPAPERS, TELLING THEM THAT MORE THAN LIKELY, CHINIQUY WOULD BE CONDEMNED AND FOUND GUILTY. THE LITTLE IRISH BOYS SELLING PAPERS PLAYED IT TO THE HILT.

EXTRA

READ ALL ABOUT IT . . .

CHINIQUY WILL BE HUNG!

CHINIQUY WILL BE HUNG!

I'LL TAKE ONE!

HERE, BOY!

THE ROMAN CATHOLICS WERE SO HAPPY TO HEAR THE NEWS THAT THEY SOLD AN EXTRA TEN THOUSAND COPIES.

IT LOOKS LIKE FATHER CHINIQUY WILL BE FOUND GUILTY.

THAT'S TOO BAD. I HAPPEN TO KNOW MR. CHINIQUY IS **NOT** GUILTY!

HOW DO YOU KNOW THAT?

I WAS THERE WHEN THE PRIEST, LEBEL, COOKED UP THE PLOT. REV. LEBEL PROMISED TO GIVE HIS SISTER, MADAM BOSSEY, 160 ACRES OF GOOD LAND IF SHE WOULD SWEAR TO A FALSE OATH . . .

AND ACCUSE MR. CHINIQUY OF A CRIME WHICH MADAM BOSSEY SAID NEVER HAPPENED.

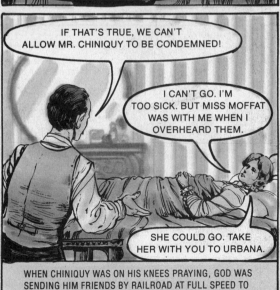

IF THAT'S TRUE, WE CAN'T ALLOW MR. CHINIQUY TO BE CONDEMNED!

I CAN'T GO. I'M TOO SICK. BUT MISS MOFFAT WAS WITH ME WHEN I OVERHEARD THEM.

SHE COULD GO. TAKE HER WITH YOU TO URBANA.

WHEN CHINIQUY WAS ON HIS KNEES PRAYING, GOD WAS SENDING HIM FRIENDS BY RAILROAD AT FULL SPEED TO SAVE HIM.

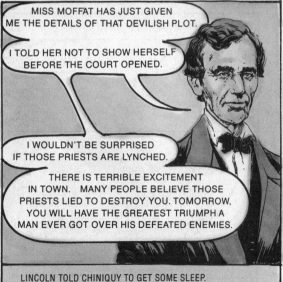

MISS MOFFAT HAS JUST GIVEN ME THE DETAILS OF THAT DEVILISH PLOT.

I TOLD HER NOT TO SHOW HERSELF BEFORE THE COURT OPENED.

I WOULDN'T BE SURPRISED IF THOSE PRIESTS ARE LYNCHED.

THERE IS TERRIBLE EXCITEMENT IN TOWN. MANY PEOPLE BELIEVE THOSE PRIESTS LIED TO DESTROY YOU. TOMORROW, YOU WILL HAVE THE GREATEST TRIUMPH A MAN EVER GOT OVER HIS DEFEATED ENEMIES.

LINCOLN TOLD CHINIQUY TO GET SOME SLEEP.

UNKNOWN TO LINCOLN AND CHINIQUY, LEBEL COULDN'T SLEEP AFTER MAKING THAT AWFUL LIE UNDER OATH.

THERE WERE ONLY TWO PERSONS WHO COULD BLOW THIS OPEN, SO HE WATCHED THE TRAINS COMING IN FROM CHICAGO.

BOTH LADIES PROMISED THEY WOULD NEVER TELL, BUT HE COULDN'T TAKE THE CHANCE.

NOT LONG AFTER SOME TRAINS ARRIVED, HE CHECKED THE HOTEL BOOK WHERE THE GUESTS SIGN IN, AND HE ALMOST HAD A HEART ATTACK WHEN HE SAW THE NAME OF THE WOMAN WHO KNEW EVERYTHING ABOUT THE PLOT.

"PHILOMENE MOFFAT." OH, GOD . . . NO!

SHE WAS COMING BACK TO THE HOTEL AFTER TELLING LINCOLN THE WHOLE STORY.

WHY ARE YOU HERE?

YOU WILL FIND OUT TOMORROW MORNING.

YOU LITTLE WRETCH. YOU'VE COME TO DESTROY ME!

YOU ARE ALREADY DESTROYED! MR. LINCOLN KNOWS EVERYTHING.

OH, MY GOD . . . OH, MY GOD!

HERE'S ONE HUNDRED DOLLARS TO GO BACK TO CHICAGO!

IF YOU OFFERED ME ENOUGH GOLD TO FILL THIS PLACE, I WOULD NOT GO!

LEBEL WOKE UP MR. SPINK (THE LAND SHARK).

SPINK, WAKE UP! WITHDRAW YOUR SUIT AGAINST CHINIQUY!

ZZZZ WHAT?

WE ARE LOST.

HE KNOWS **EVERYTHING!**

REV. LEBEL RAN TO HIS ROOM AND WOKE UP THE OTHER PRIEST, REV. CARTHUVAL. HE THREW ON HIS CLOTHES AND THEY WERE RUNNING OUT OF TOWN BEFORE THE SUN CAME UP.

NEXT MORNING

MR. SPINK, WHITE AS A GHOST, BEGGED THE JUDGE TO DROP ALL CHARGES BECAUSE HE BELIEVED MR. CHINIQUY WAS NOT GUILTY.

LINCOLN EXPLAINED WHAT HAPPENED IN A SHORT SPEECH. CHINIQUY FORGAVE THEM FOR THEIR CRIME.

MR. SPINK WAS STUCK WITH TREMENDOUS BILLS FOR TRAVELLING AND COURT COSTS. SPINK WENT TO BISHOP O'REGAN TO GET HIM TO PAY THE BILLS, BUT O'REGAN REFUSED TO PAY ONE PENNY BECAUSE CHINIQUY WAS NOT IN JAIL. SPINK WAS FINANCIALLY RUINED.

ABRAHAM LINCOLN WAS CHINIQUY'S MOST NOBLE AND DEVOTED FRIEND. HE HAD WORKED OVER A YEAR DEFENDING HIM. CHINIQUY ASKED MR. LINCOLN FOR THE BILL FOR HIS SERVICES.

MR. CHINIQUY, YOUR CASE IS UNIQUE. I HAVE NEVER MET A MAN SO CRUELLY AND UNJUSTLY PERSECUTED AS YOU HAVE BEEN.

YOUR ENEMIES ARE DEVILS IN FLESH. THEIR PLOT AGAINST YOU WAS THE MOST HELLISH I'VE EVER KNOWN.

LINCOLN SAID, "NOW, LET'S SEE WHAT YOU OWE ME. YOU OWE ME NOTHING!" CHINIQUY INSISTED, AND LINCOLN ASKED HIM FOR ONLY $50.00.

MISS MOFFAT WAS SENT BY GOD WHEN EVERYTHING WAS NEARLY LOST.

IT MAKES ME REMEMBER WHAT MY MOTHER TOLD ME WHEN I WAS YOUNG,

"OUR GOD IS A PRAYER-HEARING GOD."

MR. CHINIQUY, WHY ARE YOU CRYING?

YOU OUGHT TO BE THE HAPPIEST MAN ALIVE. YOU'VE BEATEN YOUR ENEMIES IN A GLORIOUS VICTORY.

CHINIQUY WAS FEARFUL AT WHAT THIS VICTORY WOULD COST MR. LINCOLN.

HE TOLD MR. LINCOLN, "SITTING IN THE CROWD OF THAT TRIAL, WERE TWELVE JESUIT PRIESTS FROM CHICAGO AND ST. LOUIS WHO CAME TO HEAR ME BEING SENTENCED TO PRISON."

NOTHING CAN DESCRIBE THE RAGE ON THEIR FACES WHEN YOU WRENCHED ME FROM THEIR CRUEL HANDS . . . AND THEN MADE THE COURT HOUSE TREMBLE WHEN YOU EXPOSED THE DIABOLICAL PLOT TO DESTROY ME.

WHAT I SAW IN THEIR FIENDISH EYES WAS YOUR DEATH SENTENCE.

SIGN THIS I.O.U., FATHER CHINIQUY. IT WILL BE MY DEATH WARRANT.

AFTER CHINIQUY SIGNED IT, MR. LINCOLN WAS VERY SOLEMN, AND SAID:

I KNOW THE JESUITS NEVER FORGET NOR FORSAKE (NEVER GIVE UP).

BUT A MAN MUST NOT CARE HOW AND WHERE HE DIES,

PROVIDED HE DIES AT THE POST OF HONOR AND DUTY.

IN HIS BOOK, CHINIQUY LETS US KNOW ABOUT JESUITS:

"THE JESUITS ARE A MILITARY ORGANIZATION, NOT A RELIGIOUS ORDER. THEIR CHIEF IS A GENERAL OF AN ARMY, NOT THE MERE FATHER ABBOT OF A MONASTERY. AND THE AIM OF THIS ORGANIZATION IS **POWER.** POWER IN THE MOST DESPOTIC EXERCISE. ABSOLUTE POWER, UNIVERSAL POWER, POWER TO CONTROL THE WORLD BY THE VOLITION (WILL) OF A SINGLE MAN. JESUITISM IS THE MOST ABSOLUTE OF DESPOTISMS (DICTATORSHIP); AND AT THE SAME TIME, THE GREATEST AND THE MOST ENORMOUS OF ABUSES." (THE MOST MONSTROUS HURT, INJURY AND DAMAGE)*

"THE GENERAL OF THE JESUITS INSISTS ON BEING MASTER, SOVEREIGN, OVER THE SOVEREIGN. WHEREVER THE JESUITS ARE ADMITTED THEY WILL BE MASTERS, COST WHAT IT MAY. THEIR SOCIETY IS BY NATURE DICTATORIAL, AND THEREFORE IT IS THE IRRECONCILABLE ENEMY OF ALL CONSTITUTED AUTHORITY. EVERY ACT, EVERY CRIME, HOWEVER ATROCIOUS, IS A MERITORIOUS WORK, IF COMMITTED FOR THE INTEREST OF THE SOCIETY OF THE JESUITS, OR BY THE ORDER OF ITS GENERAL."**

*MEMORIAL OF THE CAPTIVITY OF NAPOLEON AT ST. HELENA, BY GENERAL MONTHOLON, VOL. II, P. 62.
**IBID, P.174 (FOUND IN "FIFTY YEARS IN THE 'CHURCH' OF ROME," PAGE 289. PUBLISHED BY CHICK PUBLICATIONS)

THIS WAS THE ENEMY ABRAHAM LINCOLN WAS FACING. FOUR SHORT YEARS LATER, HE WOULD BE ELECTED PRESIDENT OF THE UNITED STATES.

DR. RIVERA, EX-JESUIT PRIEST SAYS THAT . . . "THE MASTER PLAN FOR THE FALL OF THE U.S. WAS UNDERWAY IN THE VATICAN. THE JESUITS AND POPE PIUS IX WERE PREPARING TO SEND FRENCH TROOPS INTO MEXICO UNDER MAXIMILLIAN TO BACK THE SOUTH WHEN THE CIVIL WAR BEGAN."

AS CHINIQUY WAS PART OF ROME'S PLAN TO ESTABLISH A COLONY TO CONTROL THE BREADBASKET OF ILLINOIS AND THE MISSISSIPPI VALLEY FOR THE VATICAN, CHINIQUY ALSO REVEALED OTHER PLANS THAT WERE UNDER WAY. A FEW YEARS EARLIER, HE HAD ATTENDED A SEMINAR IN BUFFALO, N.Y. ON "HOW THE UNITED STATES COULD BE CONTROLLED." THIS IS WHAT HE HEARD.

D'ARCY MC GEE, EDITOR OF "THE FREEMAN'S JOURNAL," OFFICIAL JOURNAL OF THE BISHOP OF NEW YORK, MADE HIS IDEAS KNOWN . . .*

I COULD LEAD THE IRISH ROMAN CATHOLICS

TO TAKE OVER THE FERTILE LANDS IN THE WEST, AND SET UP COLONIES.

NO!

THE PRIESTS DISAGREED WITH HIM.

*FIFTY YEARS IN THE CHURCH OF ROME, PG. 281, 282

SIR, WE ARE DETERMINED, LIKE YOU, TO TAKE POSSESSION OF THE UNITED STATES AND RULE THEM.

BUT WE MUST DO IT WITH THE UTMOST SECRECY AND WISDOM.

THE ANSWER IS TO CALL OUR POOR, BUT FAITHFUL, IRISH CATHOLICS FROM EVERY CORNER OF THE WORLD,

AND PUT THEM IN THE MAJOR CITIES.

LET US MULTIPLY OUR VOTES. SILENTLY AND PATIENTLY, WE MUST ASSEMBLE OUR ROMAN CATHOLICS IN THE GREAT CITIES OF THE U.S.

THE AMERICANS CONSIDER THEMSELVES A GIANT AND UNCONQUERABLE RACE.

LET US PRAY TO GOD THAT THEY MAY SLEEP ON, BELIEVING THIS, A FEW YEARS MORE.

WHAT WILL THOSE HYPOCRITICAL AND GODLESS SONS AND DAUGHTERS OF THE FANATICAL PURITANS SAY . . .

WHEN NOT A SINGLE JUDGE, TEACHER, OR POLICEMAN, WILL BE ELECTED UNLESS HE IS A DEVOTED* IRISH ROMAN CATHOLIC;

AND NOT A SINGLE SENATOR OR MEMBER OF CONGRESS WILL BE CHOSEN IF HE HAS NOT SUBMITTED TO OUR HOLY FATHER, THE POPE?

*FAITHFUL

INTERESTING NOTE: DR. RIVERA, EX-JESUIT PRIEST, ESTIMATES 80% OF OUR CONGRESSMEN TODAY ARE PRO-ROMAN CATHOLIC.

WE WLL NOT ONLY ELECT THE PRESIDENT, BUT FILL THE ARMED FORCES, AND HOLD THE KEYS TO THE PUBLIC TREASURIES.

THEN WE WILL RULE THE UNITED STATES AND LAY THEM AT THE FEET OF OUR HOLY FATHER, THE POPE.

THEN THE POPE WILL PUT AN END TO THEIR GODLESS SYSTEM OF EDUCATION AND IMPIOUS (UNGODLY) LAWS OF LIBERTY OF CONSCIENCE . . .

WHICH ARE AN INSULT TO GOD AND MAN!

BRAVO!   YES!   CLAP CLAP

LINCOLN KNEW ALL THIS WAS GOING ON WHEN HE BECAME PRESIDENT.

ABRAHAM LINCOLN WAS MOVING UP IN POLITICS. THE ONE MAN ROME HATED WAS NOMINATED ON MAY 18, 1860, BY THE REPUBLICANS TO BECOME PRESIDENT.

THE MAN NOMINATED BY THE DEMOCRATS WAS STEPHEN A. DOUGLAS. THEY CALLED HIM "THE LITTLE GIANT." LINCOLN HAD MANY DEBATES WITH HIM.

DOUGLAS WOULD COME INTO A TOWN IN A PRIVATE RAILROAD CAR, WITH THE SOUNDS OF A MILITARY BAND. HE EVEN HAD A FLAT CAR WITH A CANNON WHICH HE FIRED TO LET THE PEOPLE KNOW HE WAS COMING.

HERE COMES DOUGLAS!

BOOM

DOUGLAS

POOR OLD HONEST ABE LINCOLN USUALLY WALKED INTO TOWN.

HOWDY!

HOWDY, MR. LINCOLN.

SOMETIMES HE'D RIDE A HORSE OR COME IN RIDING IN THE CABOOSE OF A FREIGHT TRAIN.

THE ISSUE BEFORE THE PEOPLE WAS SLAVERY.

I DON'T BELIEVE THE NEGRO IS ANY KIN OF MINE AT ALL!*

IT IS WRITTEN IN THE SKY OF AMERICA THAT THE SLAVES SHALL SOME DAY BE FREE.**

STEVEN A. DOUGLAS

ABRAHAM LINCOLN

*PORTRAIT LIFE OF LINCOLN, BY MILLER, PUBLISHED 1910 BY PATRIOT PUB. CO., SPRINGFIELD, MA, PG. 26
**IBID, PG. 30

THE JESUIT-CONTROLLED PRESS BLASTED LINCOLN WITH EVERYTHING THEY HAD.

???

THE DEMOCRATIC NEWSPAPERS* NATIONWIDE, CALLED LINCOLN AN APE, A STUPID BRUTE, A MOST DANGEROUS LUNATIC, A BLOODY MONSTER, A MERCILESS TYRANT, ETC., ETC.

*PAGE 291 FIFTY YEARS IN THE "CHURCH" OF ROME

THE VATICAN ORDERED LINCOLN STOPPED AT ALL COSTS.

GOD'S HAND WAS UPON THIS NATION, AND ABRAHAM LINCOLN. ON THE 6TH OF NOVEMBER, 1860, HE WAS ELECTED PRESIDENT OF THE U.S.

THE JESUITS WERE OUT TO KILL LINCOLN, AS THEIR NUMBER ONE ASSIGNMENT.

AT THE NEWS OF LINCOLN'S ELECTION, THE SOUTH WAS OUTRAGED AND THEY REJECTED HIM AS THEIR PRESIDENT. TRADE WAS BECOMING PARALYZED. THE NATIONAL TREASURY WAS ALMOST BANKRUPT. THIS WAS THE CONDITION OF THE COUNTRY JUST BEFORE LINCOLN TOOK CONTROL OF THE NATION.

ONE MONTH LATER, SOUTH CAROLINA PULLED OUT OF THE UNITED STATES.

THE U.S. GOVERNMENT HAD A LITTLE FORT IN S. CAROLINA FLYING THE STARS AND STRIPES. IT WAS CALLED FORT SUMTER.

I FIND THAT FLAG OFFENSIVE, ESPECIALLY SINCE WE NO LONGER BELONG TO THE UNITED STATES.

THEY SHOULDN'T BE HERE.

69 MEN WERE IN THE FORT WITH ENOUGH FOOD FOR TWO WEEKS.

A SHIP WAS SENT WITH SUPPLIES TO FORT SUMTER SO THE MEN COULD HOLD THAT FORT.

THE CANNON FIRE FROM NEARBY FORT MOULTRIE TURNED THAT SHIP AROUND. THE SUPPLIES AND REINFORCEMENTS DIDN'T MAKE IT. THE NAME OF THE SHIP WAS "STAR OF THE WEST."

IMMEDIATELY, 10 OTHER STATES BROKE AWAY. IT WAS LINCOLN'S DUTY TO PULL THEM BACK.

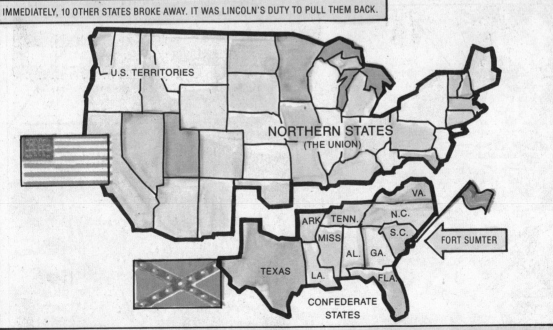

U.S. TERRITORIES

NORTHERN STATES
(THE UNION)

VA.

ARK TENN. N.C.

MISS S.C.

AL. GA.

TEXAS LA. FLA.

FORT SUMTER

CONFEDERATE STATES

ALL THIS TOOK PLACE BEFORE LINCOLN OFFICIALLY BECAME PRESIDENT. HE WAS ON HIS WAY TO WASHINGTON, D.C. FOR THE INAUGURATION (TO BE SWORN IN AS PRESIDENT), HIT-MEN WERE WAITING FOR HIM IN BALTIMORE, MARYLAND. HIS SECRET SERVICE FOUND OUT, AND GOT HIM TO WASHINGTON, D.C. ON A MIDNIGHT TRAIN.

AFTER ABRAHAM LINCOLN WAS SWORN IN, THE NEW PRESIDENT OF THE SOUTH, JEFFERSON DAVIS, ORDERED THE CONFEDERATE COMMANDER OF CHARLESTON TO ATTACK FORT SUMTER.   P.G.T. BEAUREGARD FIRED THE FIRST SHOT.*

JEFFERSON DAVIS

P.G.T. BEAUREGARD

THE FORT WAS RINGED WITH CANNON. THEY BLASTED SUMTER FOR 34 HOURS** BEFORE IT SURRENDERED AND THE MEN GAVE UP THE FORT TO THE SOUTH, AND HEADED NORTH. THE CIVIL WAR WAS ON!

*FIFTY YEARS IN THE 'CHURCH' OF ROME BY CHINIQUY, P. 299
**THE CIVIL WAR, BY CATTON, AMERICAN HERITAGE PUBLISHING CO., INC., N.Y. 1960, PG. 60.

AND SO THE NORTH AND THE SOUTH WERE READY FOR BLOOD.

ARMIES WERE RAISED. IN FOUR YEARS, SIX HUNDRED THOUSAND YOUNG AMERICANS WOULD BE DEAD.

LINCOLN CHOSE A CABINET (A GROUP OF MEN TO RUN VARIOUS DEPARTMENTS OF HIS GOVERNMENT). NOT ONE OF THESE MEN WAS HIS FRIEND.

HE CHOSE THEM BECAUSE THEY WERE THE BEST FOR THEIR JOBS. LINCOLN WAS A LONELY MAN.

THE FIRST BATTLE OF THE WAR WAS CALLED "BULL RUN," AND THE NORTH LOST. HE GOT THE BLAME.

PLEASE RESIGN, MR. PRESIDENT

NOT NOW

MORE BAD NEWS, SIR.

LINCOLN BECAME ACQUAINTED WITH GRIEF. HE'D PACE HIS ROOM AT NIGHT, ASKING GOD FOR HELP AND GUIDANCE. HE CONSTANTLY TURNED TO HIS BIBLE. HIS CLOSEST FRIEND WAS HIS LITTLE SON, WILLIE.

A TERRIBLE WEIGHT RESTED ON HIS SHOULDERS.

WHILE REPORTS POURED IN OF BOYS DYING ON THE FIELD OF BATTLE, HIS LITTLE 12-YEAR OLD SON BECAME VERY ILL. HE DIED IN THE WHITE HOUSE.

LINCOLN WAS CRUSHED. HE SAID, BETWEEN SOBS, "MY POOR BOY. HE WAS TOO GOOD FOR THIS EARTH. GOD HAS CALLED HIM HOME. I KNOW HE IS MUCH BETTER OFF IN HEAVEN. BUT WE LOVED HIM SO. IT'S HARD . . . HARD TO HAVE HIM DIE."*

*PORTRAIT LIFE OF LINCOLN, BY MILLER, PG. 68, PUBLISHED BY THE PATRIOT PUB. CO., SPRINGFIELD, MA 1910.

CHINIQUY HEARD OF A PLOT TO KILL LINCOLN, SO HE RUSHED TO WASHINGTON TO SEE HIS OLD FRIEND. LINCOLN WAS HAPPY TO SEE HIM.

YOU SEE . . .

YOUR FRIENDS, THE JESUITS, HAVEN'T KILLED ME YET.

HE COULD ONLY GIVE CHINIQUY 10 MINUTES.

HE TOLD CHINIQUY THAT WHEN MR. MORSE, THE INVENTOR OF MORSE CODE AND THE TELEGRAPH, WAS IN ROME, HE UNCOVERED A PLAN TO DESTROY THE U.S.

LINCOLN ASKED CHINIQUY IF HE WOULD JOIN HIS AMBASSADOR IN FRANCE TO INVESTIGATE THE PLOT. CHINIQUY COULD NOT LEAVE HIS LITTLE FLOCK IN ILLINOIS, AND HAD TO REFUSE THE PRESIDENT. LINCOLN UNDERSTOOD.

HE INVITED CHINIQUY BACK THE FOLLOWING DAY.

FOLLOWING DAY

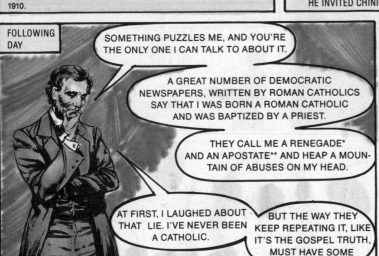

SOMETHING PUZZLES ME, AND YOU'RE THE ONLY ONE I CAN TALK TO ABOUT IT.

A GREAT NUMBER OF DEMOCRATIC NEWSPAPERS, WRITTEN BY ROMAN CATHOLICS SAY THAT I WAS BORN A ROMAN CATHOLIC AND WAS BAPTIZED BY A PRIEST.

THEY CALL ME A RENEGADE* AND AN APOSTATE** AND HEAP A MOUNTAIN OF ABUSES ON MY HEAD.

AT FIRST, I LAUGHED ABOUT THAT LIE. I'VE NEVER BEEN A CATHOLIC.

BUT THE WAY THEY KEEP REPEATING IT, LIKE IT'S THE GOSPEL TRUTH, MUST HAVE SOME MEANING.

IT DOES, MR. PRESIDENT. I CRIED WHEN I SAW THAT ARTICLE.

IT IS YOUR DEATH SENTENCE.

*RENEGADE: SOMEONE WHO DESERTS HIS RELIGION FOR A HOSTILE ONE.
**APOSTATE: ONE WHO DENOUNCES HIS OWN RELIGIOUS FAITH.

AN EX-PRIEST TOLD ME THESE NEWSPAPER STORIES ARE TO INCITE THE FANATICISM OF THE ROMAN CATHOLIC MURDERERS THEY HOPE TO FIND SOONER OR LATER.

THEY HAVE INVENTED THIS LIE OF YOU BEING BORN A ROMAN CATHOLIC AND BEING BAPTIZED BY A PRIEST. THEY WANT TO BRAND YOUR FACE WITH THE MARK OF APOSTACY.

DON'T FORGET, IN THE CHURCH OF ROME, AN APOSTATE IS AN OUTCAST AND HAS NO RIGHT TO LIVE.

THE JESUITS WANT THE ROMAN CATHOLICS TO BELIEVE YOU ARE A MONSTER . . .

AN OPEN ENEMY OF GOD AND OF HIS CHURCH . . .

THAT YOU ARE AN EX-COMMUNICATED MAN.

I HAVE BROUGHT YOU THE THEOLOGY OF ONE OF THE MOST LEARNED JESUITS OF HIS TIME . . .

WHO, WITH MANY OTHERS, SAYS THAT THE MAN WHO WILL KILL YOU WILL DO A GOOD AND HOLY WORK.

HERE IS A COPY OF A DECREE BY POPE GREGORY VII,*

WHO PROCLAIMED THAT THE KILLING OF AN APOSTATE,

OR A HERETIC, OR AN EX-COMMUNICATED MAN, AS **YOU** ARE DECLARED TO BE,

IS NOT MURDER. NO, THAT IT IS A GOOD CHRISTIAN ACTION.

THAT DECREE IS INCORPORATED IN THE CANNON LAW WHICH EVERY PRIEST MUST STUDY . . .

AND WHICH EVERY GOOD CATHOLIC MUST FOLLOW.

**"FIFTY YEARS IN THE 'CHURCH' OF ROME," BY CHINIQUY, PAGE 289.

YOU **MUST** PROTECT YOURSELF. IN THE PAST, MANY LEADERS HAVE BEEN KILLED BY JESUIT ASSASSINS!

THE CHURCH OF ROME IS ABSOLUTELY THE SAME TODAY AS SHE WAS IN THE PAST.

THE ENTIRE CATHOLIC HIERARCHY OF THE U.S. IS ON THE SIDE OF THE SOUTH, WHICH IS PROOF THAT ROME WANTS TO DESTROY THIS REPUBLIC.

MY BLOOD RUNS COLD WHEN I CONTEMPLATE THE DAY WHICH MAY COME SOONER OR LATER . . .

WHEN ROME WILL ADD TO ALL HER OTHER INIQUITIES,

THE MURDER OF ABRAHAM LINCOLN.

PRESIDENT LINCOLN SAID, "CHINIQUY, I FEEL MORE AND MORE EVERY DAY, THAT IT IS NOT THE AMERICANS OF THE SOUTH ALONE I AM FIGHTING.

"IT IS MORE AGAINST THE POPE OF ROME, HIS PERFIDIOUS JESUITS AND THEIR BLIND AND BLOODTHIRSTY SLAVES, THAN AGAINST THE REAL AMERICAN PROTESTANTS THAT WE HAVE TO DEFEND OURSELVES."

IT IS MORE A RELIGIOUS WAR THAN A CIVIL WAR!

THERE ARE ONLY A VERY FEW OF THE SOUTHERN LEADERS

WHO ARE NOT MORE OR LESS UNDER THE INFLUENCE OF THE JESUITS

THROUGH THEIR WIVES, FAMILY, RELATIONS AND FRIENDS.

SEVERAL MEMBERS OF THE FAMILY OF JEFF DAVIS BELONG TO THE "CHURCH" OF ROME.

THE MAJORITY OF THE ROMAN CATHOLIC BISHOPS, PRIESTS AND LAYMEN ARE PUBLICLY FOR SLAVERY.

THE ROMAN CATHOLIC CHIEF JUSTICE TANY SAID, "NEGROES HAVE NO RIGHTS WHICH THE WHITE MAN IS BOUND TO RESPECT."
—DRED SCOT DECISION. ("FIFTY YEARS IN THE 'CHURCH' OF ROME") BY CHINIQUY, PAGE 288

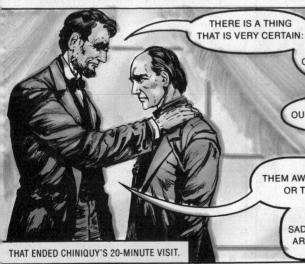

THERE IS A THING THAT IS VERY CERTAIN: IT IS THAT IF THE AMERICAN PEOPLE COULD LEARN WHAT I KNOW OF THE FIERCE HATRED OF THE GREATER PART OF THE PRIESTS OF ROME

AGAINST OUR INSTITUTIONS, OUR SCHOOLS, OUR MOST SACRED RIGHTS, AND OUR SO DEARLY BOUGHT LIBERTIES . . .

THEY WOULD DRIVE THEM AWAY TOMORROW FROM AMONG US, OR THEY WOULD SHOOT THEM AS TRAITORS.

BUT I MUST KEEP THOSE SAD SECRETS IN MY HEART. YOU ARE THE ONLY ONE TO WHOM I REVEAL THEM,

FOR I KNOW YOU LEARNED THEM BEFORE ME.

THAT ENDED CHINIQUY'S 20-MINUTE VISIT.

ABRAHAM LINCOLN SIGNED THE EMANCIPATION PROCLAMATION. THAT PIECE OF PAPER FREED 4 MILLION BLACK SLAVES.

WE'RE GONNA BE SET FREE.

IF THE NORTH WON, THEY WOULD BE SET FREE . . .

BUT IF THE SOUTH WON, WITH THE BACKING OF THE POPE, THEY WOULD REMAIN SLAVES.

THE SOUTHERNERS FOUGHT HARDER AND HATED LINCOLN THE MORE.

THE NUMBER OF DEAD BOYS WAS RISING. MOTHERS WERE WRITING TO LINCOLN IN TEARS.

MR. PRESIDENT, WILL YOU SIGN THESE PAPERS SO WE CAN EXECUTE THESE ARMY DESERTERS?

THERE ARE ALREADY TOO MANY WEEPING WIDOWS.

FOR GOD'S SAKE, DON'T ASK ME TO ADD TO THAT NUMBER, FOR I WON'T DO IT.*

*PORTRAIT LIFE OF LINCOLN, BY MILLER, PAGE 76, PUBLISHED BY THE PATRIOT PUB. CO., SPRINGFIELD, MA 1910.

AFTER THE BATTLE OF GETTYSBURG, PRESIDENT LINCOLN WENT TO WHERE THE GREAT BATTLE TOOK PLACE.

THIS IS WHERE HE FOUND CHRIST.

(REPLY TO A CLERGYMAN WHO ASKED MR. LINCOLN IF HE WAS A CHRISTIAN.) "WHEN I LEFT SPRINGFIELD, I ASKED THE PEOPLE TO PRAY FOR ME; I WAS NOT A CHRISTIAN. WHEN I BURIED MY SON, THE SEVEREST TRIAL OF MY LIFE, I WAS NOT A CHRISTIAN. BUT WHEN I SAW THE GRAVES OF THOUSANDS OF OUR SOLDIERS, I THEN AND THERE, CONSECRATED MYSELF TO CHRIST. I DO LOVE JESUS."

"WORDS OF LINCOLN," BY O. H. OLDROYD, PUBLISHED BY THE MERSHON COMPANY PRESS, 1875, PAGE 154.

IN THE WHITE HOUSE, LATE AT NIGHT, PRESIDENT LINCOLN WOULD GO DOWNSTAIRS WHERE THE BLACK SERVANTS WERE WORKING, TO READ THEM THE BIBLE, PRAY WITH THEM, AND TRY TO LEAD THEM TO CHRIST.*

THEY DEARLY LOVED THIS MAN WHO WAS SO KIND TO THEM.

*ABRAHAM LINCOLN, THE CHRISTIAN, BY W. J. JOHNSTONE, PUBLISHED BY ABINGDON PRESS, N.Y., 1913, PAGE 120.

WHEN GENERAL MEADE (A ROMAN CATHOLIC) WAS FIGHTING FOR THE NORTH, HE DEFEATED ROBERT E. LEE'S ARMY, AND WAS READY TO PURSUE THE BEATEN ARMY TO END THE WAR. LINCOLN FOUND OUT THAT A STRANGER HAD COME TO GEN. MEADE'S TENT. THAT STRANGER WAS A DISGUISED JESUIT.

MEADE

MEADE'S LOYALTY TO ROME WAS GREATER THAN HIS PATRIOTISM TO HIS UNITED STATES.

MEADE TOOK SO MUCH TIME MAKING ARRANGEMENTS THAT LEE'S ARMY GOT AWAY. MEADE ONLY CAPTURED TWO GUNS.*

LINCOLN'S ENEMIES WERE ALL AROUND HIM.

**"FIFTY YEARS IN THE 'CHURCH' OF ROME" BY CHINIQUY, PAGE 298

CHINIQUY RODE WITH PRESIDENT LINCOLN TO VISIT THE 30,000 WOUNDED PICKED UP ON THE BATTLEFIELDS AROUND RICHMOND, WHERE GENERAL GRANT WAS BREAKING THE BACK OF THE REBELLION.

CHINIQUY, THIS WAR WOULD NEVER HAVE BEEN POSSIBLE WITHOUT THE SINISTER INFLUENCE OF THE JESUITS.

WE OWE IT TO THE POPE* THAT WE NOW SEE OUR LAND REDDENED WITH THE BLOOD OF HER NOBLEST SONS.

*"FIFTY YEARS IN THE 'CHURCH' OF ROME," BY CHINIQUY, PAGE 296

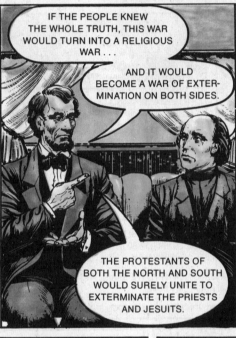

IF THE PEOPLE KNEW THE WHOLE TRUTH, THIS WAR WOULD TURN INTO A RELIGIOUS WAR . . .

AND IT WOULD BECOME A WAR OF EXTERMINATION ON BOTH SIDES.

THE PROTESTANTS OF BOTH THE NORTH AND SOUTH WOULD SURELY UNITE TO EXTERMINATE THE PRIESTS AND JESUITS.

WHEN THEY GOT BACK TO THE WHITE HOUSE.

WHAT DO YOU THINK OF THE LETTER* THE POPE WROTE TO JEFF DAVIS, CALLING HIM THE ILLUSTRIOUS AND HONORABLE PRESIDENT OF THE CONFEDERATE STATES?

THAT LETTER TELLS THE ROMAN CATHOLICS THAT YOU ARE A BLOODTHIRSTY TYRANT

BECAUSE YOU ARE FIGHTING AGAINST A GOVERNMENT WHICH THE INFALLIBLE AND HOLY POPE OF ROME RECOGNIZES AS LEGITIMATE.

THAT LETTER MEANS THAT YOU WILL GIVE AN ACCOUNT TO GOD AND MAN FOR THE BLOOD AND TEARS YOU CAUSE TO FLOW IN ORDER TO SATISFY YOUR AMBITION.

*"THE VATICAN-MOSCOW ALLIANCE," BY AVRO MANHATTAN, PAGE 271, PUBLISHED BY RALSTON-PILOT, INC., 24 ANSDELL TERRACE, KENSINGTON, LONDON W.8, ENGLAND.

THAT LETTER CHANGED EVERYTHING. FOR LINCOLN TO FIGHT THE SOUTH WAS TO FIGHT THE POPE HIMSELF, GOD AND JESUS CHRIST, IN THE EYES OF THE CATHOLICS.

IN THE NAME OF GOD, PAY MORE ATTENTION TO PROTECT YOUR PRECIOUS LIFE AND DO NOT CONTINUE TO EXPOSE YOURSELF AS YOU HAVE BEEN DOING.

PRESIDENT LINCOLN KNEW HIS ASSASSINATION WAS NEAR.

HE READ TO CHINIQUY OUT OF THE BIBLE ABOUT MOSES, IN DEUTERONOMY 3:22-28.

THE MORE I READ THOSE VERSES, IT SEEMS TO ME THAT GOD HAS WRITTEN THEM TO ME AS WELL AS MOSES.

HAS HE NOT TAKEN ME FROM MY POOR LOG CABIN BY THE HAND, AS HE DID OF MOSES IN THE REEDS OF THE NILE, TO PUT ME AT THE HEAD OF THE GREATEST AND THE MOST BLESSED OF MODERN NATIONS . . .

JUST AS HE PUT THAT PROPHET AT THE HEAD OF THE MOST BLESSED NATION OF ANCIENT TIMES?

HAS NOT GOD GRANTED ME A PRIVILEGE WHICH WAS NOT GRANTED TO ANY LIVING MAN WHEN I BROKE THE CHAINS OF 4,000,000 MEN AND MADE THEM FREE?

NOW I SEE THE END OF THIS TERRIBLE CONFLICT WITH THE SAME JOY OF MOSES,

WHEN AT THE END OF HIS TRYING 40 YEARS IN THE WILDERNESS;

AND I PRAY MY GOD TO GRANT ME TO SEE THE DAYS OF PEACE, AND UNTOLD PROSPERITY WHICH WILL FOLLOW THIS CRUEL WAR,

AS MOSES ASKED GOD TO SEE THE OTHER SIDE OF JORDAN AND ENTER THE PROMISED LAND.

BUT DO YOU KNOW THAT I HEAR IN MY SOUL, AS THE VOICE OF GOD GIVING ME THE REBUKE WHICH WAS GIVEN TO MOSES?

A SOLEMN VOICE WHICH TELLS ME THAT I WILL SEE THOSE THINGS, ONLY FROM A LONG DISTANCE AND THAT I WILL BE AMONG THE DEAD.

BUT JUST AS THE LORD HEARD NO MURMUR FROM THE LIPS OF MOSES, WHEN HE TOLD HIM THAT HE HAD TO DIE BEFORE CROSSING THE JORDAN, FOR THE SINS OF HIS PEOPLE . . .

SO I HOPE AND PRAY THAT HE WILL HEAR NO MURMUR FROM ME WHEN I FALL FOR MY NATION'S SAKE.

CHINIQUY BROKE IN TEARS, AND PRAYED WITH HIM.
BOTH KNEW HIS DEATH WAS NEAR.

AT THE FORD THEATRE ON GOOD FRIDAY, ON THE 14TH OF APRIL, 1865; AT 10 P.M., ABRAHAM LINCOLN* WAS TALKING TO HIS WIFE ABOUT HIS FUTURE PLANS. HE WANTED TO SEE THE HOLY LAND AND SEE THOSE PLACES HALLOWED BY THE FOOTPRINTS OF THE SAVIOR. HE WAS SAYING THAT THERE WAS NO CITY HE SO MUCH DESIRED TO SEE AS JERUSALEM.

AND WITH THE WORDS HALF-SPOKEN ON HIS TONGUE, THE BULLET OF HIS ASSASSIN ENTERED THE BRAIN, AND THE SOUL OF THE GREAT AND GOOD PRESIDENT WAS CARRIED BY THE ANGELS TO THE NEW JERUSALEM ABOVE.

*"ABRAHAM LINCOLN, THE CHRISTIAN," BY JOHNSTONE, ABINGDON PRESS, N.Y. 1913 PAGE 182.

THE KILLER, JOHN WILKES BOOTH, JUMPED TO THE STAGE BELOW. HIS SPUR CAUGHT IN THE FLAG AND HE BROKE HIS LEG.

HE SHOUTED TO A STUNNED AUDIENCE, HOLDING A DAGGER IN HIS HAND, "SIC SEMPER TYRANNIS" WHICH MEANS, "THUS ALWAYS TO TYRANTS." AND HE ESCAPED.

CHINIQUY SAID: "AFTER 20 YEARS OF CONSTANT AND MOST DIFFICULT RESEARCHES, I COME FEARLESSLY TODAY BEFORE THE AMERICAN PEOPLE TO SAY AND PROVE THAT THE PRESIDENT ABRAHAM LINCOLN WAS ASSASSINATED BY THE JESUITS OF ROME."**

AND CHINIQUY DOES, IN HIS BOOK, "FIFTY YEARS IN THE 'CHURCH' OF ROME," GIVE DEVASTATING EVIDENCE TO THIS FACT.

**"FIFTY YEARS IN THE 'CHURCH' OF ROME" BY CHINIQUY, PAGE 309

POPE PIUS IX AND HIS JESUITS HAD FOUND ROMAN CATHOLICS WHO WERE WILLING TO KILL THE PRESIDENT.

HEADQUARTERS FOR THIS OPERATION WAS IN THE HOUSE OF MRS. MARY SURRATT, IN WASHINGTON,* D.C. PRIESTS WERE IN THE SURRATT HOME DAY AND NIGHT.

JOHN WILKES BOOTH RODE TO DR. MUDD'S HOME TO HAVE HIS BROKEN LEG SET.

HE WAS KILLED IN A SHOOT-OUT APRIL 26TH. AROUND HIS NECK WAS A MEDAL OF THE VIRGIN MARY.** IN HIS DIARY WERE THESE WORDS: "I CAN NEVER REPENT; GOD MADE ME THE INSTRUMENT OF HIS (LINCOLN'S) PUNISHMENT."**

MARY SURRATT WAS ONE OF THE MOST DEVOUT ROMAN CATHOLIC WOMEN IN WASHINGTON, D.C.

THE DAY AFTER LINCOLN'S DEATH, HER DAUGHTER SAID "HIS DEATH WAS NO MORE THAN THE DEATH OF ANY NIGGER IN THE ARMY."**

THIS MAN STABBED SEC. OF STATE SEWARD.

LEWIS PAYNE

THIS MAN WAS TO ASSASSINATE VICE-PRESIDENT JOHNSON.

DAVEY HEROLD

THIS MAN HELPED BOOTH TO ESCAPE.

GEORGE ATZERODT

PART OF THE CONSPIRACY.

DR. SAMUEL A. MUDD

*PG 310, 50 YEARS IN ROME   **PG 310, 50 YEARS IN ROME

THE TRIAL WAS HELD. THE HIGH OFFICIALS IN THE U.S. GOVERNMENT WERE FRIGHTENED. THE ROMAN CATHOLIC ISSUE HAD TO BE AVOIDED AT ALL COSTS. IT WAS A BOMB. ALL THROUGH THE TRIAL IT WAS PLAYED DOWN. EIGHT WERE FOUND GUILTY AND FOUR WERE HUNG FOR THEIR PART IN THIS CRIME: MRS. SURRATT, LEWIS PAYNE, DAVEY HEROLD AND GEORGE ATZERODT. THE OTHERS WERE GIVEN PRISON SENTENCES.

THE POOR SLAVES OF ROME PAID THE PRICE WHILE THE JESUITS GOT OFF SCOTT FREE.

GENERAL BAKER SAID ALL CONSPIRATORS WERE ATTENDING CATHOLIC CHURCH SERVICES AND WERE BY EDUCATION ROMAN CATHOLICS.

AT THE EXECUTION, THE JESUITS ASKED THREE OF THEIR CONVERTS TO CONCEAL THAT THEY WERE ROMAN CATHOLICS FOR THE GOOD OF THE CHURCH AND BE ATTENDED BY PROTESTANT MINISTERS, FOR PUBLIC RELATIONS' SAKE, WHICH THEY AGREED TO DO.*

**"FIFTY YEARS IN THE 'CHURCH' OF ROME" BY CHINIQUY, PG. 311, 312

JOHN SURRATT, WITH THE HELP OF THE PRIESTS AND BISHOPS OF ROME, GOT OUT OF THE U.S. AND ENDED UP IN THE POPE'S PERSONAL BODYGUARDS CALLED THE ZOUAVES.

HE WAS DISCOVERED, AND THE U.S. DEMANDED HIS RETURN FROM ROME. HE WAS BROUGHT BACK FOR TRIAL. ROME SAW TO IT THAT 3 OF THE PEOPLE IN HIS JURY WERE ROMAN CATHOLICS. THEY BLOCKED THE GUILTY VERDICT OF THE OTHERS AND JOHN SURRATT HAD TO BE RELEASED. THE VATICAN HAD WON AGAIN.

DR. RIVERA, EX-JESUIT PRIEST, WAS GIVEN THE FOLLOWING INFORMATION BY JESUIT HISTORIANS WHEN HE WAS UNDER OATH. "AFTER ABRAHAM LINCOLN'S ASSASSINATION, THE VATICAN ORDERED CATHOLIC WRITERS TO IMMEDIATELY WRITE LINCOLN'S BIOGRAPHY AND DESTROY HIS REPUTATION, AND HIS CHRISTIAN TESTIMONY. PROTESTANT AUTHORS INFLUENCED BY THE VATICAN MADE THE SAME ATTACK. SOME OF THEIR CLAIMS WERE THAT LINCOLN WAS SUPPOSED TO BE AGNOSTIC, A MASON, INTO SEANCES, A FREE THINKER, AN ATHEIST, ETC., ETC. THEY WERE SUCCESSFUL! IT'S BEEN REPORTED THAT EVEN TODAY IN SOME PUBLIC SCHOOLS, CATHOLIC TEACHERS ARE TURNING BLACK STUDENTS AGAINST LINCOLN, CALLING HIM A PHONEY. ROME NEVER GIVES UP."

*SEE "DOUBLE-CROSS," CRUSADERS, VOLUME 13.

WE SAW HOW ABRAHAM LINCOLN FOUND CHRIST ON THE BATTLEFIELD AT GETTYSBURG, AND NOW WE GO BACK TO SEE WHAT HAPPENED TO CHINIQUY THAT CAUSED THE GREATEST BLOW ROME HAS EVER SUFFERED IN THE UNITED STATES.

WHEN CHINIQUY WON HIS COURT CASE AGAINST SPINK AND BISHOP O'REGAN, IT CAUSED SHOCK WAVES IN THE ROMAN SYSTEM.

CHINIQUY MUST BE DESTROYED. HE IS TOO MUCH TROUBLE!

IT'S IN THE NEWSPAPERS EVERYWHERE

ONLY TWO OTHER PRIESTS DID THIS IN HISTORY, AND THEY WERE LUTHER AND JOHN KNOX!

THEY SOUNDED THE ALARM THAT CHINIQUY WAS A REBEL, BUT BEFORE THEY WOULD CRUSH HIM, THEY WOULD TRY TO GET HIM TO SUBMIT TO O'REGAN.

HIS TWO BEST FRIENDS FROM CANADA WERE SENT TO ST. ANNE TO INVESTIGATE WHY CHINIQUY WAS STILL SAYING MASS AFTER HE HAD BEEN EX-COMMUNICATED.

YOU SEE, BISHOP O'REGAN NEVER SIGNED THE PAPER THAT EX-COMMUNICATED ME.

HE LIED TO US.

WE WILL BACK YOU, CHINIQUY. YOU ARE A GOOD PRIEST.

THEY ASKED CHINIQUY TO SIGN A LETTER OF SUBMISSION TO O'REGAN, WHICH HE DID. HIS FRIENDS WERE DELIGHTED.

AFTER THE INVESTIGATION THEY TOLD THE PEOPLE OF ST. ANNE THAT BOTH THEY AND CHINIQUY WERE INNOCENT.

MR. BRASSARD WILL BE YOUR PASTOR, AND MR. CHINIQUY WILL REMAIN WITH YOU.

HE SIGNED THE ACT OF SUBMISSION THAT WILL BRING PEACE.

CHINIQUY'S DEAR FRIEND WENT TO CHICAGO TO STRAIGHTEN OUT O'REGAN.

O'REGAN CUT THE CANADIAN PRIEST TO SHREDS. THE PRIEST LOOKED LIKE A GHOST. HE SENT FOR CHINIQUY AND BRASSARD TO JOIN HIM IN CHICAGO.

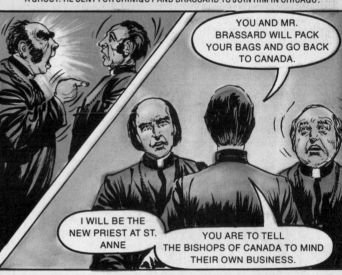

YOU AND MR. BRASSARD WILL PACK YOUR BAGS AND GO BACK TO CANADA.

I WILL BE THE NEW PRIEST AT ST. ANNE

YOU ARE TO TELL THE BISHOPS OF CANADA TO MIND THEIR OWN BUSINESS.

CHINIQUY SAID:

YOU ARE A TRAITOR AND A JUDAS.

BISHOP O'REGAN TEMPTED YOU, AND YOU SOLD ME OUT.

I ADVISE YOU **NEVER** TO GO BACK TO ST. ANNE.

ONE OF HIS LAST TWO FRIENDS HAD JUST DOUBLE-CROSSED HIM. THE ONLY ONE LEFT IN THE FAITH HE TRUSTED WAS BRASSARD.

CHINIQUY SAID GOOD-BYE TO HIS LAST FRIEND. HE ASKED MR. BRASSARD TO TELL THEM BACK IN CANADA HOW THIS TRAITOR HAD MADE THINGS WORSE.

GOOD-BYE, ME DEAR FRIEND.

SOB

CHINIQUY WOULD STAY WITH HIS PEOPLE TO PREACH THE GOSPEL AND FIGHT THOSE WHO WOULD DESTROY THEIR FAITH.

THE PEOPLE OF ST. ANNE PUBLISHED THE WHOLE STORY IN THE NEWSPAPERS IN CANADA AND THE U.S.

CHINIQUY'S LAST FRIEND, UNDER TREMENDOUS PRESSURES FROM THE BISHOPS, PUBLICLY DENOUNCED CHINIQUY. ANOTHER JUDAS HAD DOUBLE-CROSSED HIM.

MY LAST FRIEND IN THE PRIESTHOOD IS GONE . . .

ROME HAS DESTROYED MR. BRASSARD LIKE ALL THE OTHERS.

GOD WAS WARNING CHINIQUY TO PULL OUT OF ROME, TIME AND TIME AGAIN.

NOW HE WAS ALL ALONE.

CHINIQUY WROTE TO THE POPE. HE SENT HIM COPIES OF ALL THE NEWSPAPERS AND LETTERS.

BUT IN CASE IT GOT LOST, HE SENT A DUPLICATE SET TO THE EMPEROR OF FRANCE, NAPOLEON III.

NAPOLEON III HAD PUT THE POPE BACK IN ROME AND THE POPE APPRECIATED IT.

THIS FRENCH EMPEROR FOUND OUT THAT ONE FRENCHMAN HAD BEEN MISTREATED IN CHINA. NAPOLEON WAS SO MAD · · ·

THAT HE SENT AN ARMY TO PUNISH THE EMPEROR OF CHINA.

NAPOLEON III RECEIVED CHINIQUY'S PACKAGE FROM HIS AMBASSADOR. HE READ IT AND SAW THAT CHINIQUY WAS A FRENCHMAN, THAT HIS GRANDFATHER FOUGHT FOR FRANCE AS A CAPTAIN IN THE NAVY, AND FOR GALLANT SERVICE WAS AWARDED LANDS IN CANADA WHICH FELL INTO THE HANDS OF THE BRITISH. HE, LIKE NAPOLEON, HAD FRENCH BLOOD AND WAS A ROMAN CATHOLIC. IT PUSHED NAPOLEON'S BUTTON.

WHO IS THIS BISHOP O'REGAN WHO DARED TO MISTREAT THESE POOR FRENCH CANADIANS? HE HAS TRAMPLED MY COUNTRYMEN UNDER HIS FEET.

HE HAS RUINED THEM AND GIVEN ALL THEY HAD TO THE IRISH!

WHAT THE CHINESE DID TO THAT ONE FRENCHMAN IS NOTHING COMPARED TO WHAT BISHOP O'REGAN HAS DONE!

TO CALM DOWN NAPOLEON, THE POPE SENT FOR O'REGAN.

I'LL SEE TO IT THAT THE POPE MAKES BISHOP O'REGAN PAY FOR THESE CRIMES ! ! !

THIS IS AN OUTRAGE TO MY COUNTRYMEN, AND TO **FRANCE!**

O'REGAN WAS DUMPED. HE LOST HIS POSITION IN CHICAGO AND WAS TRANSFERRED TO ANOTHER DIOCESE.

I NEVER HEARD OF DORA!

IT WAS A DIOCESE THAT HAD BEEN EXTINCT FOR OVER 1200 YEARS. IT WAS LIKE BEING SENT TO THE MOON.

O'REGAN WENT TO PARIS AND DREW OUT HUNDREDS OF THOUSANDS OF DOLLARS HE HAD STOLEN FROM THE ROMAN CATHOLICS IN CHICAGO AND HAD DEPOSITED IN PARIS BANKS.

FOR THE LIFE OF ME, I CAN'T FIGURE OUT . . .

HOW NAPOLEON GOT INVOLVED IN THIS THING.

HE WENT TO IRELAND AND BECAME A BANKER. HE DIED IN 1865.

A NEW BISHOP CAME TO CHICAGO.

CHINIQUY SENT HIM A LETTER OF SUBMISSION WHICH HE RECEIVED, AND WROTE A GLOWING LETTER TO CHINIQUY IN RETURN. CHINIQUY WAS DELIGHTED.

A FEW DAYS LATER

MY LORD, BISHOP . . .

DID YOU SEE WHAT CHINIQUY WROTE IN HIS LETTER OF SUBMISSION?

HE SUBMITS TO THE BISHOP'S AUTHORITY **ONLY** ACCORDING TO THE WORD OF GOD AND THE GOSPEL OF JESUS CHRIST.

I DIDN'T NOTICE THAT.

HE IS A PROTESTANT IN DISGUISE. YOU **MUST** GET YOUR LETTER BACK FROM HIM.

CHINIQUY WAS CALLED BACK TO CHICAGO. THE BISHOP ASKED FOR THE LETTER AND THREW IT INTO THE FIRE.

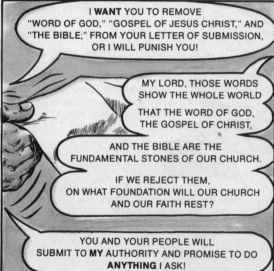

I **WANT** YOU TO REMOVE "WORD OF GOD," "GOSPEL OF JESUS CHRIST," AND "THE BIBLE;" FROM YOUR LETTER OF SUBMISSION, OR I WILL PUNISH YOU!

MY LORD, THOSE WORDS SHOW THE WHOLE WORLD

THAT THE WORD OF GOD, THE GOSPEL OF CHRIST,

AND THE BIBLE ARE THE FUNDAMENTAL STONES OF OUR CHURCH.

IF WE REJECT THEM, ON WHAT FOUNDATION WILL OUR CHURCH AND OUR FAITH REST?

YOU AND YOUR PEOPLE WILL SUBMIT TO **MY** AUTHORITY AND PROMISE TO DO **ANYTHING** I ASK!

THAT IS NOT AN ACT OF SUBMISSION. IT IS AN ACT OF ADORATION!

I REFUSE TO GIVE IT.

IF IT BE SO, SIR . . . YOU CAN NO LONGER BE A ROMAN CATHOLIC PRIEST.

CHINIQUY RAISED HIS HANDS TO HEAVEN AND SAID, "MAY GOD ALMIGHTY BE FOREVER BLESSED."

CHINIQUY LEFT. HIS CAREER WAS GONE. HE HAD BEEN KICKED OUT OF THE CHURCH HE SO GREATLY LOVED.

IN HIS HOTEL ROOM, THE AWFUL TRUTH HIT HIM. HE SAID . . .

MY CHURCH COULD **NOT** BE THE CHURCH OF CHRIST.

NO PROTESTANT OR ENEMY OF THE CHURCH SAID IT; IT CAME FROM THE LIPS OF HER MOST LEARNED BISHOPS.

CHINIQUY SAID, "MY CHURCH WAS THE DEADLY AND IRRECONCILABLE ENEMY OF THE WORD OF GOD."

ON HIS KNEES HE REALIZED THAT GOD HAD CALLED HIM TO COME OUT YEARS AGO.

MY GOD . . .

MY GOD, THE CHURCH OF ROME

IS **NOT** MY CHURCH!

WHEN I HAD A CHOICE BETWEEN GIVING UP THAT CHURCH

OR THE BIBLE,

I COULD NOT GIVE UP THE WORD OF GOD!

BUT, O LORD, WHERE IS THY CHURCH?

OH, SPEAK! WHERE MUST I GO TO BE SAVED?

CHINIQUY WAS IN GREAT DARKNESS. THERE WAS NO PLACE TO GO. ROME HAD DESTROYED HIM.

HE TRIED TO COMMIT SUICIDE, BUT GOD STOPPED HIM. HE WAS AT THE END OF HIS ROPE. IN A COLD SWEAT, HE CRIED TO JESUS FOR HELP. HE OPENED HIS BIBLE AND SAW THESE WORDS:

"YE ARE BOUGHT WITH A PRICE; BE NOT YE THE SERVANTS OF MEN." (I COR. 7:23)

IT HIT AS LIGHT. THE KNOWLEDGE THAT THE GREAT MYSTERY WAS PERFECT SALVATION THROUGH CHRIST ALONE FLOODED HIS MIND.

JESUS BOUGHT ME . . . THEN HE SAVED ME.

AND IF SO, I AM SAVED — PERFECTLY SAVED.

JESUS CANNOT SAVE ME BY HALF.

JESUS IS MY GOD.

THE WORKS OF GOD ARE PERFECT.

MY SALVATION MUST THEN BE . . . PERFECT SALVATION!

HOW DID HE SAVE ME?

THE ANSWER WAS . . .

HE BOUGHT YOU WITH HIS BLOOD SHED ON THE CROSS.

IT WAS NOT BY MY PENANCES, MY PRAYERS TO MARY AND THE SAINTS, MY CONFESSIONS AND INDULGENCES, NOT EVEN BY THE FLAMES OF PURGATORY AS I HAD PREACHED.

IN THAT INSTANT, ALL THINGS WHICH AS A ROMAN CATHOLIC I HAD TO BELIEVE TO BE SAVED . . .

VANISHED.

ALL THE RIDICULOUS CEREMONIES BY WHICH THE POOR ROMAN CATHOLICS ARE SO CRUELLY DECEIVED SUCH AS INDULGENCES, SCAPULARIES, AURICULAR CONFESSION, INVOCATIONS OF THE VIRGIN, HOLY WATER, MASSES, PURGATORY, ETC., GIVEN AS A MEANS OF SALVATION

VANISHED FROM MY MIND LIKE A HIGH TOWER THAT'S STRUCK IN ITS FOUNDATIONS AND CRUMBLES TO THE GROUND.

JESUS ALONE REMAINED IN MY MIND AS THE SAVIOR OF MY SOUL.

HE CRIED FOR JESUS TO TAKE AWAY HIS SINS. HE DID!

CHINIQUY WAS BORN AGAIN WHEN HE DISCOVERED THAT SALVATION WAS A GIFT FROM GOD.

THE BIBLE SAYS:
BY GRACE ARE YE SAVED THROUGH FAITH; AND THAT NOT OF YOURSELVES: IT IS THE **GIFT OF GOD:** NOT OF WORKS, LEST ANY MAN SHOULD BOAST. (EPH. 2:8,9)

HE TOOK THE TRAIN BACK TO ST. ANNE TO TELL HIS PEOPLE WHAT HAD HAPPENED. WOULD THEY LISTEN TO HIM?

CHINIQUY TOLD THEM WHAT HAD HAPPENED IN CHICAGO. HE TOLD THEM WHAT HAD HAPPENED IN THE HOTEL. HE TOLD THEM NOT TO FOLLOW HIM, BUT CHRIST.

SUDDENLY A CHANGE CAME OVER THE PEOPLE. THEY WEPT.

LET ALL WHO THINK IT IS BETTER TO FOLLOW JESUS CHRIST THAN THE POPE,

BETTER TO FOLLOW THE WORD OF GOD THAN THE TRADITIONS OF MEN;

LET ALL OF YOU WHO WANT ME TO REMAIN HERE,

TO PREACH TO YOU NOTHING BUT THE WORD OF GOD AS WE FIND IT IN THE GOSPEL OF CHRIST . . .

RISE UP!

THE MULTITUDE AROSE . . . MORE THAN A THOUSAND.

THEIR CHAINS TO ROME WERE BROKEN.

CHINIQUY WAS USED OF GOD TO WIN THOUSANDS OF ROMAN CATHOLICS TO CHRIST IN THE U.S., CANADA AND AUSTRALIA

THE PLOT OF ROME TO WIN ILLINOIS AND THE MISSISSIPPI VALLEY FOR THE VATICAN BACKFIRED. REVIVAL BROKE OUT AND THE GREAT AREA BECAME ALIVE TO THE GOSPEL, AND THE BIBLE BELT WAS FORMED.

HIS CHURCH AT ST. ANNE JOINED THE BIBLE BELIEVING PRESBYTERIAN CHURCH BACK WHEN THE PRESBYTERIAN CHURCH WAS COMPLETELY SOLD OUT FOR CHRIST.

HERETIC!

KILL CHINIQUY!

STOP HIM

CHINIQUY WAS THE ENEMY OF ROME UNTIL HE DIED. HE SUFFERED ATTACKS, LAW SUITS AND COURT APPEARANCES WHILE HE LED HIS BELOVED ROMAN CATHOLICS TO CHRIST.

GOD USED CHINIQUY IN A MIGHTY WAY.

TODAY ROME WEARS A NEW FACE BEFORE THE CHRISTIANS. HAS SHE CHANGED?

DR. RIVERA, AN EX-JESUIT PRIEST, SAYS "NO!

ROME STILL CONTROLS GOVERNMENTS OF THE WORLD THROUGH HER JESUITS AND HER INTRIGUES.

THE U.S. IS STILL HER TARGET AND SHE IS STILL PARTICIPATING IN THE ASSASSINATION OF WORLD LEADERS WHO DO NOT GO ALONG WITH HER."

THE ONLY THING THAT IS CHANGED IS THAT THE GREAT BOOKS EXPOSING ROME HAVE DISAPPEARED, THE PROTESTANTS HAVE BEEN LULLED INTO BOWING DOWN TO THE POPE OF ROME, EVEN IN THE PULPITS. ONLY GOD CAN RAISE THEM UP AGAIN.

60 MILLION ROMAN CATHOLICS HAVE BEEN EXPOSED TO THE BIBLE WHICH IS THE OPEN DOOR TO LEAD THEM TO THE ONLY ONE WHO CAN SAVE THEM. THE FIELDS ARE WHITE UNTO HARVEST.

JESUS SAID, "I AM THE WAY, THE TRUTH AND THE LIFE: NO MAN COMETH UNTO THE FATHER BUT BY ME." (JOHN 14:6)

FOR GOD SO LOVED THE WORLD . . . JOHN 3:16

JESUS IS NOT A DEAD CHRIST ON A CRUCIFIX. HE IS ALIVE IN HEAVEN AND HE LOVES YOU. HE SHED HIS PRECIOUS BLOOD TO WASH AWAY YOUR SINS, AND HE WANTS YOU TO REIGN WITH HIM.